SUPPLEMENT
NDS®

National Design Specification®

Design Values for Wood Construction

2012 EDITION

AMERICAN WOOD COUNCIL

Copyright © 2011, 2012
American Wood Council

National Design Specification (NDS) Supplement: Design Values for Wood Construction 2012 Edition

First Web Version: November 2011
Second Web Version: February 2014

First Printing: October 2012
Second Printing: November 2013
Third Printing: February 2015
Fourth Printing: June 2017

ISBN 978-0-9827380-3-0

Printed in the United States of America

Introduction

This Supplement is a compendium of reference design values for structural sawn lumber, structural glued laminated timber, and round timber piles and poles. These reference design values have been obtained from the organizations responsible for establishing design values for these products. Reference design values in this Supplement are provided as a courtesy for use with the design provisions of the *National Design Specification® (NDS®) for Wood Construction*, 2012 Edition.

Lumber

Reference design values for lumber in this Supplement are obtained from grading rules published by seven agencies: National Lumber Grades Authority (a Canadian agency), Northeastern Lumber Manufacturers Association, Northern Softwood Lumber Bureau, Redwood Inspection Service, Southern Pine Inspection Bureau, West Coast Lumber Inspection Bureau, and Western Wood Products Association. Grading rules promulgated by these agencies, including reference design values therein, have been approved by the Board of Review of the American Lumber Standard Committee and certified for conformance with U.S. Department of Commerce Voluntary Product Standard PS 20-10 (American Softwood Lumber Standard).

Reference design values for most species and grades of visually graded dimension lumber are based on provisions of ASTM Standard D 1990-07 (Establishing Allowable Properties for Visually Graded Dimension Lumber from In-Grade Tests of Full-Size Specimens). Reference design values for visually graded timbers, decking, and some species and grades of dimension lumber are based on provisions of ASTM Standard D 245-06 (2011) (Establishing Structural Grades and Related Allowable Properties for Visually Graded Lumber). Methods in ASTM Standard D 245 involve adjusting strength properties of small clear specimens of wood, as given in ASTM Standard D 2555-06 (Establishing Clear Wood Strength Values), for effects of knots, slope of grain, splits, checks, size, duration of load, moisture content, and other influencing factors, to obtain reference design values applicable to normal conditions of service. Lumber structures designed on the basis of working stresses derived from ASTM Standard D 245 procedures and standard design criteria have a long history of satisfactory performance.

Reference design values for machine stress rated (MSR) lumber and machine evaluated lumber (MEL) are based on nondestructive testing of individual pieces. Certain visual grade requirements also apply to such lumber. The stress rating system used for MSR and MEL lumber is regularly checked by the responsible grading agency for conformance to established certification and quality control procedures.

For additional information on development and applicability of lumber reference design values, grading rules published by individual agencies and referenced ASTM Standards should be consulted.

Structural Glued Laminated Timber

Reference design values in this Supplement for structural glued laminated timber are developed and published by the American Institute of Timber Construction (AITC) and APA–The Engineered Wood Association (APA) in accordance with principles originally established by the U.S. Forest Products Laboratory in the early 1950s. These principles involve adjusting strength properties of clear straight grained lumber to account for knots, slope of grain, density, size of member, number of laminations, and other factors unique to laminated timber.

Specific methods used to establish reference design values have been periodically revised and improved to reflect results of tests of large structural glued laminated timber members conducted by the U.S. Forest Products Laboratory and other accredited testing agencies. The performance history of structures made with structural glued laminated timber conforming to AITC or APA specifications and manufactured in accordance with American National Standard ANSI/AITC A190.1-2007 (Structural Glued Laminated Timber) has demonstrated the validity of methods used to establish structural glued laminated timber reference design values.

Round Timber Piles and Poles

Reference design values in this Supplement for round timber piles and poles are developed by the Timber Piling Council of the Southern Pressure Treaters' Association in accordance with principles originally established by the U.S. Forest Products Laboratory in the early 1950s and contained in ASTM D 2899-03 (Standard Practice for Establishing Allowable Stresses for Round Timber Piles) and ASTM D 3200-74 (2005) (Standard Practice for Establishing Allowable Stresses for Round Timber Construction Poles), respectively. These principles involve adjusting strength properties of clear straight grained poles to account for knots, slope of grain, density, size of member, and other factors unique to timber poles.

Specific methods used to establish reference design values are contained in D 2899 and are used by D 3200. These methods have been revised to reflect results of full-size tests of timber piles.

Conditions of Use

Reference design values presented in this Supplement

are for normal load duration under dry conditions of service. Because the strength of wood varies with conditions under which it is used, these reference design values should only be applied in conjunction with appropriate design and service recommendations from the *NDS*. Additionally, reference design values in this Supplement apply only to material identified by the grade mark of, or certificate of inspection issued by, a grading or inspection bureau or agency recognized as being competent.

American Wood Council

TABLE OF CONTENTS

LIST OF TABLES

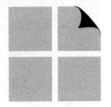

SAWN LUMBER GRADING AGENCIES

1.1 List of Sawn Lumber Grading Agencies

Following is a list of agencies certified by the American Lumber Standard Committee Board of Review (as of 2011) for inspection and grading of untreated lumber under the rules indicated. For the most up-to-date list of certified agencies contact:

American Lumber Standard Committee
P.O. Box 210
Germantown, Maryland 20875-0210
www.alsc.org

Rules Writing Agencies

Rules for which grading is authorized

Northeastern Lumber Manufacturers Association (NELMA) .... NELMA, NLGA, NSLB, SPIB, WCLIB, WWPA
  272 Tuttle Road, P.O. Box 87A, Cumberland Center, Maine 04021
Northern Softwood Lumber Bureau (NSLB) .... NLGA, NSLB, WCLIB, WWPA
  272 Tuttle Road, P.O. Box 87A, Cumberland Center, Maine 04021
Redwood Inspection Service (RIS).. RIS, WCLIB, WWPA
  818 Grayson Road, Suite 201, Pleasant Hill, California 94523
Southern Pine Inspection Bureau (SPIB)... NELMA, NLGA, NSLB, SPIB, WCLIB, WWPA
  4709 Scenic Highway, Pensacola, Florida 32504
West Coast Lumber Inspection Bureau (WCLIB) ....NLGA, RIS, SPIB, WCLIB, WWPA
  6980 SW Varnes Road, P.O. Box 23145, Tigard, Oregon 97223
Western Wood Products Association (WWPA).. NELMA, NLGA, RIS, SPIB, WCLIB, WWPA
  522 SW Fifth Avenue, Suite 500, Portland, Oregon 97204
National Lumber Grades Authority (NLGA)
  13401-108th Avenue, Suite 105, Surrey, BC, Canada V3T 5T3

Non-Rules Writing Agencies

American Institute of Timber Construction ....NLGA, SPIB, WCLIB, WWPA
Continental Inspection Agency, LLC... NLGA, RIS, WCLIB, WWPA
Pacific Lumber Inspection Bureau, Inc.. NLGA, RIS, WCLIB, WWPA
Renewable Resource Associates, Inc. .... NELMA, NLGA, NSLB, SPIB, WCLIB, WWPA
Stafford Inspection and Consulting, LLC.. NELMA, NLGA, NSLB, SPIB, WCLIB, WWPA
Timber Products Inspection .... NELMA, NLGA, NSLB, RIS, SPIB, WCLIB, WWPA

Alberta Forest Products Association .... NLGA
Canadian Mill Services Association .... NLGA, WWPA
Canadian Softwood Inspection Agency, Inc. .... NLGA, WCLIB, WWPA
Central Forest Products Association .... NELMA, NLGA
Council of Forest Industries... NLGA, WWPA
Macdonald Inspection .... NLGA, WCLIB, WWPA
Maritime Lumber Bureau .... NELMA, NLGA
Newfoundland and Labrador Lumber Producers Association .... NLGA
Ontario Forest Industries Association – Home of CLA Grading and Inspection .... NELMA, NLGA
Ontario Lumber Manufacturers Agency .... NELMA, NLGA
Quebec Forest Industry Council .... NELMA, NLGA

SPECIES COMBINATIONS

AMERICAN WOOD COUNCIL

2.1 List of Sawn Lumber Species Combinations

Species or Species Combination	Species That May Be Included in Combination	Grading Rules Agencies	Design Values Provided in Tab
Alaska Cedar		WCLIB	4A
Alaska Hemlock		WWPA	4A
Alaska Spruce	Alaska Sitka Spruce Alaska White Spruce	WWPA	4A
Alaska Yellow Cedar		WCLIB, WWPA	4A
Aspen	Big Tooth Aspen Quaking Aspen	NELMA NSLB WWPA	4A
Baldcypress		SPIB	4A, 4D
Balsam Fir		NELMA NSLB	4D, 4E
Beech-Birch-Hickory	American Beech Bitternut Hickory Mockernut Hickory Nutmeg Hickory Pecan Hickory Pignut Hickory Shagbark Hickory Shellbark Hickory Sweet Birch Water Hickory Yellow Birch	NELMA	4A, 4D
Coast Sitka Spruce		NLGA	4A, 4D, 4E
Coast Species	Amabilis Fir Coast Sitka Spruce Douglas Fir Western Hemlock Western Larch	NLGA	4E
Cottonwood		NSLB	4A
Douglas Fir-Larch	Douglas Fir Western Larch	WCLIB WWPA	4A, 4C, 4D, 4E
Douglas Fir-Larch (North)	Douglas Fir Western Larch	NLGA	4A, 4C, 4D, 4E
Douglas Fir-South		WWPA	4A, 4C, 4D, 4E
Eastern Hemlock		NELMA NSLB	4D
Eastern Hemlock-Balsam Fir	Balsam Fir Eastern Hemlock Tamarack	NELMA	4A
Eastern Hemlock-Tamarack	Eastern Hemlock Tamarack	NELMA NSLB	4A, 4D, 4E
Eastern Hemlock-Tamarack (North)	Eastern Hemlock Tamarack	NLGA	4D, 4E

Species or Species Combination	Species That May Be Included in Combination	Grading Rules Agencies	Design Values Provided in Tables
Eastern Softwoods	Balsam Fir Black Spruce Eastern Hemlock Eastern White Pine Jack Pine Norway (Red) Pine Pitch Pine Red Spruce Tamarack White Spruce	NELMA NSLB	4A
Eastern Spruce	Black Spruce Red Spruce White Spruce	NELMA NSLB	4D, 4E
Eastern White Pine		NELMA NSLB	4A, 4D, 4E
Eastern White Pine (North)		NLGA	4E
Hem-Fir	California Red Fir Grand Fir Noble Fir Pacific Silver Fir Western Hemlock White Fir	WCLIB WWPA	4A, 4C, 4D, 4E
Hem-Fir (North)	Amabilis Fir Western Hemlock	NLGA	4A, 4C, 4D, 4E
Mixed Maple	Black Maple Red Maple Silver Maple Sugar Maple	NELMA	4A, 4D
Mixed Oak	All Oak Species graded under NELMA rules	NELMA	4A, 4D

Mixed Southern Pine	Any species in the Southern Pine species combination, plus either or both of the following:
	    Pond Pine
	    Virginia Pine
		SPIB	4B, 4C, 4D

Mountain Hemlock		WWPA, WCLIB	4D
Northern Pine	Jack Pine Norway (Red) Pine Pitch Pine	NELMA NSLB	4D, 4E
Northern Red Oak	Black Oak Northern Red Oak Pin Oak Scarlet Oak	NELMA	4A, 4D
Northern Species	Any species graded under NLGA rules except Red Alder, White Birch, and Norway Spruce	NLGA	4A, 4C, 4E
Northern White Cedar		NELMA	4A, 4D, 4E
Ponderosa Pine		NLGA	4D, 4E

2.1 List of Sawn Lumber Species Combinations (Cont.)

Species or Species Combination	Species That May Be Included in Combination	Grading Rules Agencies	Design Values Provided in Tables
Red Maple		NELMA	4A, 4D
Red Oak	Black Oak Cherrybark Oak Laurel Oak Northern Red Oak Pin Oak Scarlet Oak Southern Red Oak Water Oak Willow Oak	NELMA	4A, 4D
Red Pine		NLGA	4D, 4E
Redwood		RIS	4A, 4D, 4E
Sitka Spruce		WWPA, WCLIB	4D, 4E
Southern Pine	Loblolly Pine Longleaf Pine Shortleaf Pine Slash Pine	SPIB	4B, 4C, 4D, 4E
Spruce-Pine-Fir	Alpine Fir Balsam Fir Black Spruce Engelmann Spruce Jack Pine Lodgepole Pine Red Spruce White Spruce	NLGA	4A, 4C, 4D, 4E
Spruce-Pine-Fir (South)	Balsam Fir Black Spruce Engelmann Spruce Jack Pine Lodgepole Pine Norway (Red) Pine Red Spruce Sitka Spruce White Spruce	NELMA NSLB WCLIB WWPA	4A, 4C, 4D, 4E
Western Cedars	Alaska Cedar Incense Cedar Port Orford Cedar Western Red Cedar	WCLIB WWPA	4A, 4C, 4D, 4E
Western Cedars (North)	Pacific Coast Yellow Cedar Western Red Cedar	NLGA	4D, 4E
Western Hemlock		WWPA, WCLIB	4D, 4E
Western Hemlock (North)		NLGA	4D, 4E
Western White Pine		NLGA	4D, 4E

Species or Species Combination	Species That May Be Included in Combination	Grading Rules Agencies	Design Values Provided in Tables
Western Woods	Any species in the Douglas Fir-Larch, Douglas Fir-South, Hem-Fir, and Spruce-Pine-Fir (South) species combinations, plus any or all of the following: 　　Alpine Fir 　　Idaho White Pine 　　Mountain Hemlock 　　Ponderosa Pine 　　Sugar Pine	WCLIB WWPA	4A, 4C, 4D, 4E
White Oak	Bur Oak Chestnut Oak Live Oak Overcup Oak Post Oak Swamp Chestnut Oak Swamp White Oak White Oak	NELMA	4A, 4D
Yellow Cedar		NLGA	4A
Yellow Poplar		NSLB	4A

2

SPECIES COMBINATIONS

2.2 List of Non-North American Sawn Lumber Species Combinations

Species or Species Combination	Species That May Be Included in Combination	Grading Rules Agency	Design Values Provided in Tables
Austrian Spruce - Austria & The Czech Republic		WCLIB	4F
Douglas Fir - France & Germany		WCLIB	4F
Douglas Fir/European Larch - Austria, The Czech Republic, & Bavaria	Douglas Fir European Larch	WCLIB	4F
Montane Pine - South Africa		WCLIB	4F
Norway Spruce - Estonia, Latvia, & Lithuania		WCLIB	4F
Norway Spruce - Finland		WCLIB	4F
Norway Spruce - Germany, NE France, & Switzerland		WCLIB	4F
Norway Spruce - Romania & the Ukraine		WCLIB	4F
Norway Spruce - Sweden		WCLIB	4F
Scots Pine - Austria, The Czech Republic, Romania, & the Ukraine		WCLIB	4F
Scots Pine - Estonia, Latvia, & Lithuania		WCLIB	4F
Scots Pine - Finland		WCLIB	4F
Scots Pine - Germany*		WCLIB	4F
Scots Pine - Sweden		WCLIB	4F
Silver Fir (*Abies alba*) - Germany, NE France, & Switzerland		WCLIB	4F
Southern Pine - Misiones Argentina		SPIB	4F
Southern Pine - Misiones Argentina, Free of Heart Center and Medium Grain Density		SPIB	4F

* Does not include states of Baden-Wurttemburg and Saarland.

2.3 List of Structural Glued Laminated Timber Species Combinations

Species or Species Group	Symbol	Species That May Be Included in Group	Design Values Provided in Tables
Alaska Cedar	AC	Alaska Cedar	5A, 5B
Douglas Fir-Larch	DF	Douglas Fir, Western Larch	5A, 5B
Eastern Spruce	ES	Black Spruce Red Spruce White Spruce	5A
Hem-Fir	HF	California Red Fir Grand Fir Noble Fir Pacific Silver Fir Western Hemlock White Fir	5A, 5B
Softwood Species	SW	Alpine Fir Balsam Fir Black Spruce Douglas Fir Douglas Fir South Engelmann Spruce Idaho White Pine Jack Pine Lodgepole Pine Mountain Hemlock Ponderosa Pine Red Spruce Sugar Pine Western Larch Western Red Cedar White Spruce	5A, 5B
Southern Pine	SP	Loblolly Pine Longleaf Pine Shortleaf Pine Slash Pine	5A, 5B
Spruce-Pine-Fir	SPF	Alpine Fir Balsam Fir Black Spruce Engelmann Spruce Jack Pine Lodgepole Pine Norway Pine Red Spruce Sitka Spruce White Spruce	5A

SPECIES COMBINATIONS

2

Species or Species Group	Symbol	Species That May Be Included in Group	Design Values Provided in Tables
Group A Hardwoods	A	Ash, White Beech, American Birch, Sweet Birch, Yellow Hickory, Bitternut Hickory, Mockernut Hickory, Nutmeg Hickory, Pecan Hickory, Pignut Hickory, Shagbark Hickory, Shellbark Hickory, Water Oak, Northern Red Oak, White	5C, 5D

Group B Hardwoods	B	Elm, Rock
		Maple, Black
		Maple, Red
		Mixed Oak:
		    Black
		    Bur
		    Cherrybark
		    Chestnut
		    Laurel
		    Live
		    Northern Red
		    Overcup
		    Pin
		    Post
		    Scarlet
		    Southern Red
		    Swamp Chestnut
		    Swamp White
		    Water
		    White
		Sweetgum
			5C, 5D

Group C Hardwoods	C	Ash, Black Elm, American Tupulo, Water Yellow Poplar	5C, 5D

Group D Hardwoods	D	Aspen, Bigtooth
		Aspen, Quaking
		Cottonwood, Eastern
		Mixed Maple:
		    Black
		    Red
		    Silver
		    Sugar
			5C, 5D

SECTION PROPERTIES

3

AMERICAN WOOD COUNCIL

3.1 Section Properties of Sawn Lumber and Structural Glued Laminated Timber

3.1.1 Standard Sizes of Sawn Lumber

Details regarding the dressed sizes of various species of lumber in the grading rules of the agencies which formulate and maintain such rules. The dressed sizes in Table 1A conform to the sizes set forth in U.S. Department of Commerce Voluntary Product Standard PS 20-10 (American Softwood Lumber Standard). While these sizes are generally available on a commercial basis, it is good practice to consult the local lumber dealer to determine what sizes are on hand or can be readily secured.

Dry lumber is defined as lumber which has been seasoned to a moisture content of 19% or less. Green lumber is defined as lumber having a moisture content in excess of 19%.

3.1.2 Properties of Standard Dressed Sizes

Certain mathematical expressions of the properties or elements of sections are used in design calculations for various member shapes and loading conditions. The section properties for selected standard sizes of boards, dimension lumber, and timbers are given in Table 1B. Section properties for selected standard sizes of structural glued laminated timber are given in Tables 1C and 1D.

3.1.3 Definitions

NEUTRAL AXIS, in the cross section of a beam, is the line on which there is neither tension nor compression stress.

MOMENT OF INERTIA, I, of the cross section of a beam is the sum of the products of each of its elementary areas multiplied by the square of their distance from the neutral axis of the section.

SECTION MODULUS, S, is the moment of inertia divided by the distance from the neutral axis to the extreme fiber of the section.

CROSS SECTION is a section taken through the member perpendicular to its longitudinal axis.

The following symbols and formulas apply to rectangular beam cross sections:

X-X = neutral axis for edgewise bending (load applied to narrow face)

Y-Y = neutral axis for flatwise bending (load applied to wide face)

b = breadth (thickness) of rectangular bending member, in.

d = depth (width) of rectangular bending member, in.

$A = bd$ = area of cross section, in.^{2}

c = distance from neutral axis to extreme fiber of cross section, in.

$I_x = bd^3/12$ = moment of inertia about the X-X axis, in.^{4}

$I_y = db^3/12$ = moment of inertia about the Y-Y axis, in.^{4}

$r_x = \sqrt{I_x/A} = d/\sqrt{12}$ = radius of gyration about the X-X axis, in.

$r_y = \sqrt{I_y/A} = b/\sqrt{12}$ = radius of gyration about the Y-Y axis, in.

$S_x = I_x/c = bd^2/6$ = section modulus about the X-X axis, in.^{3}

$S_y = I_y/c = db^2/6$ = section modulus about the Y-Y axis, in.^{3}

The following formula shall be used to determine the density in lbs/ft^3 of wood:

$$\text{density} = 62.4\left[\frac{G}{1+G(0.009)(m.c.)}\right]\left[1+\frac{m.c.}{100}\right]$$

where:

G = specific gravity of wood

m.c. = moisture content of wood, %

Figure 1A Dimensions for Rectangular Cross Section

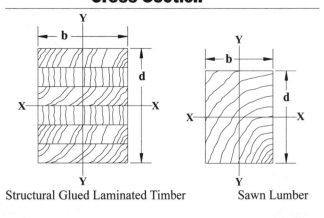

Structural Glued Laminated Timber   Sawn Lumber

Table 1A Nominal and Minimum Dressed Sizes of Sawn Lumber

Item	Thickness (in.)			Face Widths (in.)		
	Nominal	Minimum dressed		Nominal	Minimum dressed	
		Dry	Green		Dry	Green
Boards	3/4	5/8	11/16	2	1-1/2	1-9/16
	1	3/4	25/32	3	2-1/2	2-9/16
	1-1/4	1	1-1/32	4	3-1/2	3-9/16
	1-1/2	1-1/4	1-9/32	5	4-1/2	4-5/8
				6	5-1/2	5-5/8
				7	6-1/2	6-5/8
				8	7-1/4	7-1/2
				9	8-1/4	8-1/2
				10	9-1/4	9-1/2
				11	10-1/4	10-1/2
				12	11-1/4	11-1/2
				14	13-1/4	13-1/2
				16	15-1/4	15-1/2
Dimension Lumber	2	1-1/2	1-9/16	2	1-1/2	1-9/16
	2-1/2	2	2-1/16	3	2-1/2	2-9/16
	3	2-1/2	2-9/16	4	3-1/2	3-9/16
	3-1/2	3	3-1/16	5	4-1/2	4-5/8
	4	3-1/2	3-9/16	6	5-1/2	5-5/8
	4-1/2	4	4-1/16	8	7-1/4	7-1/2
				10	9-1/4	9-1/2
				12	11-1/4	11-1/2
				14	13-1/4	13-1/2
				16	15-1/4	15-1/2
Timbers	5 & 6 thick	1/2 off	1/2 off	5 & 6 wide	1/2 off	1/2 off
	7-15 thick	3/4 off	1/2 off	7-15 wide	3/4 off	1/2 off
	≥16 thick	1 off	1/2 off	≥16 wide	1 off	1/2 off

3

SECTION PROPERTIES

Table 1B   Section Properties of Standard Dressed (S4S) Sawn Lumber

Nominal Size b x d	Standard Dressed Size (S4S) b x d in. x in.	Area of Section A in.^{2}	X-X AXIS Section Modulus S_{xx} in.^{3}	X-X AXIS Moment of Inertia I_{xx} in.^{4}	Y-Y AXIS Section Modulus S_{yy} in.^{3}	Y-Y AXIS Moment of Inertia I_{yy} in.^{4}	Approximate weight in pounds per linear foot (lbs/ft) of piece when density of wood equals: 25 lbs/ft^3	30 lbs/ft^3	35 lbs/ft^3	40 lbs/ft^3	45 lbs/ft^3	50 lbs/ft^3
Boards[1]												
1 x 3	3/4 x 2-1/2	1.875	0.781	0.977	0.234	0.088	0.326	0.391	0.456	0.521	0.586	0.651
1 x 4	3/4 x 3-1/2	2.625	1.531	2.680	0.328	0.123	0.456	0.547	0.638	0.729	0.820	0.911
1 x 6	3/4 x 5-1/2	4.125	3.781	10.40	0.516	0.193	0.716	0.859	1.003	1.146	1.289	1.432
1 x 8	3/4 x 7-1/4	5.438	6.570	23.82	0.680	0.255	0.944	1.133	1.322	1.510	1.699	1.888
1 x 10	3/4 x 9-1/4	6.938	10.70	49.47	0.867	0.325	1.204	1.445	1.686	1.927	2.168	2.409
1 x 12	3/4 x 11-1/4	8.438	15.82	88.99	1.055	0.396	1.465	1.758	2.051	2.344	2.637	2.930
Dimension Lumber (see NDS 4.1.3.2) and Decking (see NDS 4.1.3.5)												
2 x 3	1-1/2 x 2-1/2	3.750	1.56	1.953	0.938	0.703	0.651	0.781	0.911	1.042	1.172	1.302
2 x 4	1-1/2 x 3-1/2	5.250	3.06	5.359	1.313	0.984	0.911	1.094	1.276	1.458	1.641	1.823
2 x 5	1-1/2 x 4-1/2	6.750	5.06	11.39	1.688	1.266	1.172	1.406	1.641	1.875	2.109	2.344
2 x 6	1-1/2 x 5-1/2	8.250	7.56	20.80	2.063	1.547	1.432	1.719	2.005	2.292	2.578	2.865
2 x 8	1-1/2 x 7-1/4	10.88	13.14	47.63	2.719	2.039	1.888	2.266	2.643	3.021	3.398	3.776
2 x 10	1-1/2 x 9-1/4	13.88	21.39	98.93	3.469	2.602	2.409	2.891	3.372	3.854	4.336	4.818
2 x 12	1-1/2 x 11-1/4	16.88	31.64	178.0	4.219	3.164	2.930	3.516	4.102	4.688	5.273	5.859
2 x 14	1-1/2 x 13-1/4	19.88	43.89	290.8	4.969	3.727	3.451	4.141	4.831	5.521	6.211	6.901
3 x 4	2-1/2 x 3-1/2	8.75	5.10	8.932	3.646	4.557	1.519	1.823	2.127	2.431	2.734	3.038
3 x 5	2-1/2 x 4-1/2	11.25	8.44	18.98	4.688	5.859	1.953	2.344	2.734	3.125	3.516	3.906
3 x 6	2-1/2 x 5-1/2	13.75	12.60	34.66	5.729	7.161	2.387	2.865	3.342	3.819	4.297	4.774
3 x 8	2-1/2 x 7-1/4	18.13	21.90	79.39	7.552	9.440	3.147	3.776	4.405	5.035	5.664	6.293
3 x 10	2-1/2 x 9-1/4	23.13	35.65	164.9	9.635	12.04	4.015	4.818	5.621	6.424	7.227	8.030
3 x 12	2-1/2 x 11-1/4	28.13	52.73	296.6	11.72	14.65	4.883	5.859	6.836	7.813	8.789	9.766
3 x 14	2-1/2 x 13-1/4	33.13	73.15	484.6	13.80	17.25	5.751	6.901	8.051	9.201	10.35	11.50
3 x 16	2-1/2 x 15-1/4	38.13	96.90	738.9	15.89	19.86	6.619	7.943	9.266	10.59	11.91	13.24
4 x 4	3-1/2 x 3-1/2	12.25	7.15	12.51	7.146	12.51	2.127	2.552	2.977	3.403	3.828	4.253
4 x 5	3-1/2 x 4-1/2	15.75	11.81	26.58	9.188	16.08	2.734	3.281	3.828	4.375	4.922	5.469
4 x 6	3-1/2 x 5-1/2	19.25	17.65	48.53	11.23	19.65	3.342	4.010	4.679	5.347	6.016	6.684
4 x 8	3-1/2 x 7-1/4	25.38	30.66	111.1	14.80	25.90	4.405	5.286	6.168	7.049	7.930	8.811
4 x 10	3-1/2 x 9-1/4	32.38	49.91	230.8	18.89	33.05	5.621	6.745	7.869	8.993	10.12	11.24
4 x 12	3-1/2 x 11-1/4	39.38	73.83	415.3	22.97	40.20	6.836	8.203	9.570	10.94	12.30	13.67
4 x 14	3-1/2 x 13-1/4	46.38	102.41	678.5	27.05	47.34	8.051	9.661	11.27	12.88	14.49	16.10
4 x 16	3-1/2 x 15-1/4	53.38	135.66	1034	31.14	54.49	9.266	11.12	12.97	14.83	16.68	18.53
Timbers (5" x 5" and larger)[2]												
Post and Timber (see NDS 4.1.3.4 and 4.1.5.3)												
5 x 5	4-1/2 x 4-1/2	20.25	15.19	34.17	15.19	34.17	3.516	4.219	4.922	5.625	6.328	7.031
6 x 6	5-1/2 x 5-1/2	30.25	27.73	76.26	27.73	76.26	5.252	6.302	7.352	8.403	9.453	10.50
6 x 8	5-1/2 x 7-1/2	41.25	51.56	193.4	37.81	104.0	7.161	8.594	10.03	11.46	12.89	14.32
8 x 8	7-1/2 x 7-1/2	56.25	70.31	263.7	70.31	263.7	9.766	11.72	13.67	15.63	17.58	19.53
8 x 10	7-1/2 x 9-1/2	71.25	112.8	535.9	89.06	334.0	12.37	14.84	17.32	19.79	22.27	24.74
10 x 10	9-1/2 x 9-1/2	90.25	142.9	678.8	142.9	678.8	15.67	18.80	21.94	25.07	28.20	31.34
10 x 12	9-1/2 x 11-1/2	109.3	209.4	1204	173.0	821.7	18.97	22.76	26.55	30.35	34.14	37.93
12 x 12	11-1/2 x 11-1/2	132.3	253.5	1458	253.5	1458	22.96	27.55	32.14	36.74	41.33	45.92
12 x 14	11-1/2 x 13-1/2	155.3	349.3	2358	297.6	1711	26.95	32.34	37.73	43.13	48.52	53.91
14 x 14	13-1/2 x 13-1/2	182.3	410.1	2768	410.1	2768	31.64	37.97	44.30	50.63	56.95	63.28
14 x 16	13-1/2 x 15-1/2	209.3	540.6	4189	470.8	3178	36.33	43.59	50.86	58.13	65.39	72.66
16 x 16	15-1/2 x 15-1/2	240.3	620.6	4810	620.6	4810	41.71	50.05	58.39	66.74	75.08	83.42
16 x 18	15-1/2 x 17-1/2	271.3	791.1	6923	700.7	5431	47.09	56.51	65.93	75.35	84.77	94.18
18 x 18	17-1/2 x 17-1/2	306.3	893.2	7816	893.2	7816	53.17	63.80	74.44	85.07	95.70	106.3
18 x 20	17-1/2 x 19-1/2	341.3	1109	10813	995.3	8709	59.24	71.09	82.94	94.79	106.6	118.5
20 x 20	19-1/2 x 19-1/2	380.3	1236	12049	1236	12049	66.02	79.22	92.4	105.6	118.8	132.0
20 x 22	19-1/2 x 21-1/2	419.3	1502	16150	1363	13285	72.79	87.34	101.9	116.5	131.0	145.6
22 x 22	21-1/2 x 21-1/2	462.3	1656	17806	1656	17806	80.25	96.30	112.4	128.4	144.5	160.5
22 x 24	21-1/2 x 23-1/2	505.3	1979	23252	1810	19463	87.72	105.3	122.8	140.3	157.9	175.4
24 x 24	23-1/2 x 23-1/2	552.3	2163	25415	2163	25415	95.88	115.1	134.2	153.4	172.6	191.8

Nominal Size b x d	Standard Dressed Size (S4S) b x d in. x in.	Area of Section A in.^{2}	X-X AXIS		Y-Y AXIS		Approximate weight in pounds per linear foot (lbs/ft) of piece when density of wood equals:					
			Section Modulus S_{xx} in.^{3}	Moment of Inertia I_{xx} in.^{4}	Section Modulus S_{yy} in.^{3}	Moment of Inertia I_{yy} in.^{4}	25 lbs/ft^3	30 lbs/ft^3	35 lbs/ft^3	40 lbs/ft^3	45 lbs/ft^3	50 lbs/ft^3
Beams & Stringers (see NDS 4.1.3.3 and 4.1.5.3)												
6 x 10	5-1/2 x 9-1/2	52.25	82.73	393.0	47.90	131.7	9.071	10.89	12.70	14.51	16.33	18.14
6 x 12	5-1/2 x 11-1/2	63.25	121.2	697.1	57.98	159.4	10.98	13.18	15.37	17.57	19.77	21.96
6 x 14	5-1/2 x 13-1/2	74.25	167.1	1128	68.06	187.2	12.89	15.47	18.05	20.63	23.20	25.78
6 x 16	5-1/2 x 15-1/2	85.25	220.2	1707	78.15	214.9	14.80	17.76	20.72	23.68	26.64	29.60
6 x 18	5-1/2 x 17-1/2	96.25	280.7	2456	88.23	242.6	16.71	20.05	23.39	26.74	30.08	33.42
6 x 20	5-1/2 x 19-1/2	107.3	348.6	3398	98.31	270.4	18.62	22.34	26.07	29.79	33.52	37.24
6 x 22	5-1/2 x 21-1/2	118.3	423.7	4555	108.4	298.1	20.53	24.64	28.74	32.85	36.95	41.06
6 x 24	5-1/2 x 23-1/2	129.3	506.2	5948	118.5	325.8	22.44	26.93	31.41	35.90	40.39	44.88
8 x 12	7-1/2 x 11-1/2	86.3	165.3	950.5	107.8	404.3	14.97	17.97	20.96	23.96	26.95	29.95
8 x 14	7-1/2 x 13-1/2	101.3	227.8	1538	126.6	474.6	17.58	21.09	24.61	28.13	31.64	35.16
8 x 16	7-1/2 x 15-1/2	116.3	300.3	2327	145.3	544.9	20.18	24.22	28.26	32.29	36.33	40.36
8 x 18	7-1/2 x 17-1/2	131.3	382.8	3350	164.1	615.2	22.79	27.34	31.90	36.46	41.02	45.57
8 x 20	7-1/2 x 19-1/2	146.3	475.3	4634	182.8	685.5	25.39	30.47	35.55	40.63	45.70	50.78
8 x 22	7-1/2 x 21-1/2	161.3	577.8	6211	201.6	755.9	27.99	33.59	39.19	44.79	50.39	55.99
8 x 24	7-1/2 x 23-1/2	176.3	690.3	8111	220.3	826.2	30.60	36.72	42.84	48.96	55.08	61.20
10 x 14	9-1/2 x 13-1/2	128.3	288.6	1948	203.1	964.5	22.27	26.72	31.17	35.63	40.08	44.53
10 x 16	9-1/2 x 15-1/2	147.3	380.4	2948	233.1	1107	25.56	30.68	35.79	40.90	46.02	51.13
10 x 18	9-1/2 x 17-1/2	166.3	484.9	4243	263.2	1250	28.86	34.64	40.41	46.18	51.95	57.73
10 x 20	9-1/2 x 19-1/2	185.3	602.1	5870	293.3	1393	32.16	38.59	45.03	51.46	57.89	64.32
10 x 22	9-1/2 x 21-1/2	204.3	731.9	7868	323.4	1536	35.46	42.55	49.64	56.74	63.83	70.92
10 x 24	9-1/2 x 23-1/2	223.3	874.4	10274	353.5	1679	38.76	46.51	54.26	62.01	69.77	77.52
12 x 16	11-1/2 x 15-1/2	178.3	460.5	3569	341.6	1964	30.95	37.14	43.32	49.51	55.70	61.89
12 x 18	11-1/2 x 17-1/2	201.3	587.0	5136	385.7	2218	34.94	41.93	48.91	55.90	62.89	69.88
12 x 20	11-1/2 x 19-1/2	224.3	728.8	7106	429.8	2471	38.93	46.72	54.51	62.29	70.08	77.86
12 x 22	11-1/2 x 21-1/2	247.3	886.0	9524	473.9	2725	42.93	51.51	60.10	68.68	77.27	85.85
12 x 24	11-1/2 x 23-1/2	270.3	1058	12437	518.0	2978	46.92	56.30	65.69	75.07	84.45	93.84
14 x 18	13-1/2 x 17-1/2	236.3	689.1	6029	531.6	3588	41.02	49.22	57.42	65.63	73.83	82.03
14 x 20	13-1/2 x 19-1/2	263.3	855.6	8342	592.3	3998	45.70	54.84	63.98	73.13	82.27	91.41
14 x 22	13-1/2 x 21-1/2	290.3	1040	11181	653.1	4408	50.39	60.47	70.55	80.63	90.70	100.8
14 x 24	13-1/2 x 23-1/2	317.3	1243	14600	713.8	4818	55.08	66.09	77.11	88.13	99.14	110.2
16 x 20	15-1/2 x 19-1/2	302.3	982.3	9578	780.8	6051	52.47	62.97	73.46	83.96	94.45	104.9
16 x 22	15-1/2 x 21-1/2	333.3	1194	12837	860.9	6672	57.86	69.43	81.00	92.57	104.1	115.7
16 x 24	15-1/2 x 23-1/2	364.3	1427	16763	941.0	7293	63.24	75.89	88.53	101.2	113.8	126.5
18 x 22	17-1/2 x 21-1/2	376.3	1348	14493	1097	9602	65.32	78.39	91.45	104.5	117.6	130.6
18 x 24	17-1/2 x 23-1/2	411.3	1611	18926	1199	10495	71.40	85.68	99.96	114.2	128.5	142.8
20 x 24	19-1/2 x 23-1/2	458.3	1795	21089	1489	14521	79.56	95.47	111.4	127.3	143.2	159.1

1. According to the Southern Pine Inspection Bureau's (SPIB) Standard Grading Rules for Southern Pine Lumber: Section 265 stress rated boards:
- Industrial 55 (IND 55) shall be graded as per No. 1 dimension
- Industrial 45 (IND 45) shall be graded as per No. 2 dimension
- Industrial 26 (IND 26) shall be graded as per No. 3 dimension

See Table 4B for Southern Pine dimension lumber design values.

2. Neither Redwood nor Southern Pine are classified as Beams and Stringers or Posts and Timbers.

3

SECTION PROPERTIES

Table 1C Section Properties of *Western Species* Structural Glued Laminated Timber

Depth d (in.)	Area A (in.^{2})	X-X Axis				Y-Y Axis	
		I_x (in.^{4})	S_x (in.^{3})	r_x (in.)		I_y (in.^{4})	S_y (in.^{3})
2-1/2 in. Width						**(r_y = 0.722 in.)**	
6	15.00	45.00	15.00	1.732		7.813	6.250
7-1/2	18.75	87.89	23.44	2.165		9.766	7.813
9	22.50	151.9	33.75	2.598		11.72	9.375
10-1/2	26.25	241.2	45.94	3.031		13.67	10.94
12	30.00	360.0	60.00	3.464		15.63	12.50
13-1/2	33.75	512.6	75.94	3.897		17.58	14.06
15	37.50	703.1	93.75	4.330		19.53	15.63
16-1/2	41.25	935.9	113.4	4.763		21.48	17.19
18	45.00	1215	135.0	5.196		23.44	18.75
19-1/2	48.75	1545	158.4	5.629		25.39	20.31
21	52.50	1929	183.8	6.062		27.34	21.88
3-1/8 in. Width						**(r_y = 0.902 in.)**	
6	18.75	56.25	18.75	1.732		15.26	9.766
7-1/2	23.44	109.9	29.30	2.165		19.07	12.21
9	28.13	189.8	42.19	2.598		22.89	14.65
10-1/2	32.81	301.5	57.42	3.031		26.70	17.09
12	37.50	450.0	75.00	3.464		30.52	19.53
13-1/2	42.19	640.7	94.92	3.897		34.33	21.97
15	46.88	878.9	117.2	4.330		38.15	24.41
16-1/2	51.56	1170	141.8	4.763		41.96	26.86
18	56.25	1519	168.8	5.196		45.78	29.30
19-1/2	60.94	1931	198.0	5.629		49.59	31.74
21	65.63	2412	229.7	6.062		53.41	34.18
22-1/2	70.31	2966	263.7	6.495		57.22	36.62
24	75.00	3600	300.0	6.928		61.04	39.06
3-1/2 in. Width						**(r_y = 1.010 in.)**	
6	21.00	63.00	21.00	1.732		21.44	12.25
7-1/2	26.25	123.0	32.81	2.165		26.80	15.31
9	31.50	212.6	47.25	2.598		32.16	18.38
10-1/2	36.75	337.6	64.31	3.031		37.52	21.44
12	42.00	504.0	84.00	3.464		42.88	24.50
13-1/2	47.25	717.6	106.3	3.897		48.23	27.56
15	52.50	984.4	131.3	4.330		53.59	30.63
16-1/2	57.75	1310	158.8	4.763		58.95	33.69
18	63.00	1701	189.0	5.196		64.31	36.75
19-1/2	68.25	2163	221.8	5.629		69.67	39.81
21	73.50	2701	257.3	6.062		75.03	42.88
22-1/2	78.75	3322	295.3	6.495		80.39	45.94
24	84.00	4032	336.0	6.928		85.75	49.00

Table 1C Section Properties of *Western Species* Structural Glued Laminated Timber (Cont.)

Depth	Area	X-X Axis			Y-Y Axis	
d (in.)	A (in.^{2})	I_x (in.^{4})	S_x (in.^{3})	r_x (in.)	I_y (in.^{4})	S_y (in.^{3})
5-1/8 in. Width					**(r_y = 1.479 in.)**	
6	30.75	92.25	30.75	1.732	67.31	26.27
7-1/2	38.44	180.2	48.05	2.165	84.13	32.83
9	46.13	311.3	69.19	2.598	101.0	39.40
10-1/2	53.81	494.4	94.17	3.031	117.8	45.96
12	61.50	738.0	123.0	3.464	134.6	52.53
13-1/2	69.19	1051	155.7	3.897	151.4	59.10
15	76.88	1441	192.2	4.330	168.3	65.66
16-1/2	84.56	1919	232.5	4.763	185.1	72.23
18	92.25	2491	276.8	5.196	201.9	78.80
19-1/2	99.94	3167	324.8	5.629	218.7	85.36
21	107.6	3955	376.7	6.062	235.6	91.93
22-1/2	115.3	4865	432.4	6.495	252.4	98.50
24	123.0	5904	492.0	6.928	269.2	105.1
25-1/2	130.7	7082	555.4	7.361	286.0	111.6
27	138.4	8406	622.7	7.794	302.9	118.2
28-1/2	146.1	9887	693.8	8.227	319.7	124.8
30	153.8	11530	768.8	8.660	336.5	131.3
31-1/2	161.4	13350	847.5	9.093	353.4	137.9
33	169.1	15350	930.2	9.526	370.2	144.5
34-1/2	176.8	17540	1017	9.959	387.0	151.0
36	184.5	19930	1107	10.39	403.8	157.6
5-1/2 in. Width					**(r_y = 1.588 in.)**	
6	33.00	99.00	33.00	1.732	83.19	30.25
7-1/2	41.25	193.4	51.56	2.165	104.0	37.81
9	49.50	334.1	74.25	2.598	124.8	45.38
10-1/2	57.75	530.6	101.1	3.031	145.6	52.94
12	66.00	792.0	132.0	3.464	166.4	60.50
13-1/2	74.25	1128	167.1	3.897	187.2	68.06
15	82.50	1547	206.3	4.330	208.0	75.63
16-1/2	90.75	2059	249.6	4.763	228.8	83.19
18	99.00	2673	297.0	5.196	249.6	90.75
19-1/2	107.3	3398	348.6	5.629	270.4	98.31
21	115.5	4245	404.3	6.062	291.2	105.9
22-1/2	123.8	5221	464.1	6.495	312.0	113.4
24	132.0	6336	528.0	6.928	332.8	121.0
25-1/2	140.3	7600	596.1	7.361	353.5	128.6
27	148.5	9021	668.3	7.794	374.3	136.1
28-1/2	156.8	10610	744.6	8.227	395.1	143.7
30	165.0	12380	825.0	8.660	415.9	151.3
31-1/2	173.3	14330	909.6	9.093	436.7	158.8
33	181.5	16470	998.3	9.526	457.5	166.4
34-1/2	189.8	18820	1091	9.959	478.3	173.9
36	198.0	21380	1188	10.39	499.1	181.5

3

SECTION PROPERTIES

Table 1C   Section Properties of *Western Species* Structural Glued Laminated Timber (Cont.)

Depth d (in.)	Area A (in.^{2})	X-X Axis			Y-Y Axis	
		I_x (in.^{4})	S_x (in.^{3})	r_x (in.)	I_y (in.^{4})	S_y (in.^{3})
		6-3/4 in. Width			**(r_y = 1.949 in.)**	
7-1/2	50.63	237.3	63.28	2.165	192.2	56.95
9	60.75	410.1	91.13	2.598	230.7	68.34
10-1/2	70.88	651.2	124.0	3.031	269.1	79.73
12	81.00	972.0	162.0	3.464	307.5	91.13
13-1/2	91.13	1384	205.0	3.897	346.0	102.5
15	101.3	1898	253.1	4.330	384.4	113.9
16-1/2	111.4	2527	306.3	4.763	422.9	125.3
18	121.5	3281	364.5	5.196	461.3	136.7
19-1/2	131.6	4171	427.8	5.629	499.8	148.1
21	141.8	5209	496.1	6.062	538.2	159.5
22-1/2	151.9	6407	569.5	6.495	576.7	170.9
24	162.0	7776	648.0	6.928	615.1	182.3
25-1/2	172.1	9327	731.5	7.361	653.5	193.6
27	182.3	11070	820.1	7.794	692.0	205.0
28-1/2	192.4	13020	913.8	8.227	730.4	216.4
30	202.5	15190	1013	8.660	768.9	227.8
31-1/2	212.6	17580	1116	9.093	807.3	239.2
33	222.8	20210	1225	9.526	845.8	250.6
34-1/2	232.9	23100	1339	9.959	884.2	262.0
36	243.0	26240	1458	10.39	922.6	273.4
37-1/2	253.1	29660	1582	10.83	961.1	284.8
39	263.3	33370	1711	11.26	999.5	296.2
40-1/2	273.4	37370	1845	11.69	1038	307.5
42	283.5	41670	1985	12.12	1076	318.9
43-1/2	293.6	46300	2129	12.56	1115	330.3
45	303.8	51260	2278	12.99	1153	341.7
46-1/2	313.9	56560	2433	13.42	1192	353.1
48	324.0	62210	2592	13.86	1230	364.5
49-1/2	334.1	68220	2757	14.29	1269	375.9
51	344.3	74620	2926	14.72	1307	387.3
52-1/2	354.4	81400	3101	15.16	1346	398.7
54	364.5	88570	3281	15.59	1384	410.1
55-1/2	374.6	96160	3465	16.02	1422	421.5
57	384.8	104200	3655	16.45	1461	432.8
58-1/2	394.9	112600	3850	16.89	1499	444.2
60	405.0	121500	4050	17.32	1538	455.6

Table 1C Section Properties of *Western Species* Structural Glued Laminated Timber (Cont.)

Depth d (in.)	Area A (in.^{2})	X-X Axis				Y-Y Axis	
		I_x (in.^{4})	S_x (in.^{3})	r_x (in.)		I_y (in.^{4})	S_y (in.^{3})
			8-3/4 in. Width			(r_y = 2.526 in.)	
9	78.75	531.6	118.1	2.598		502.4	114.8
10-1/2	91.88	844.1	160.8	3.031		586.2	134.0
12	105.0	1260	210.0	3.464		669.9	153.1
13-1/2	118.1	1794	265.8	3.897		753.7	172.3
15	131.3	2461	328.1	4.330		837.4	191.4
16-1/2	144.4	3276	397.0	4.763		921.1	210.5
18	157.5	4253	472.5	5.196		1005	229.7
19-1/2	170.6	5407	554.5	5.629		1089	248.8
21	183.8	6753	643.1	6.062		1172	268.0
22-1/2	196.9	8306	738.3	6.495		1256	287.1
24	210.0	10080	840.0	6.928		1340	306.3
25-1/2	223.1	12090	948.3	7.361		1424	325.4
27	236.3	14350	1063	7.794		1507	344.5
28-1/2	249.4	16880	1185	8.227		1591	363.7
30	262.5	19690	1313	8.660		1675	382.8
31-1/2	275.6	22790	1447	9.093		1759	402.0
33	288.8	26200	1588	9.526		1842	421.1
34-1/2	301.9	29940	1736	9.959		1926	440.2
36	315.0	34020	1890	10.39		2010	459.4
37-1/2	328.1	38450	2051	10.83		2094	478.5
39	341.3	43250	2218	11.26		2177	497.7
40-1/2	354.4	48440	2392	11.69		2261	516.8
42	367.5	54020	2573	12.12		2345	535.9
43-1/2	380.6	60020	2760	12.56		2428	555.1
45	393.8	66450	2953	12.99		2512	574.2
46-1/2	406.9	73310	3153	13.42		2596	593.4
48	420.0	80640	3360	13.86		2680	612.5
49-1/2	433.1	88440	3573	14.29		2763	631.6
51	446.3	96720	3793	14.72		2847	650.8
52-1/2	459.4	105500	4020	15.16		2931	669.9
54	472.5	114800	4253	15.59		3015	689.1
55-1/2	485.6	124700	4492	16.02		3098	708.2
57	498.8	135000	4738	16.45		3182	727.3
58-1/2	511.9	146000	4991	16.89		3266	746.5
60	525.0	157500	5250	17.32		3350	765.6

Table 1C   Section Properties of *Western Species* Structural Glued Laminated Timber (Cont.)

Depth d (in.)	Area A (in.^{2})	X-X Axis			Y-Y Axis	
		I_x (in.^{4})	S_x (in.^{3})	r_x (in.)	I_y (in.^{4})	S_y (in.^{3})
10-3/4 in. Width					(r_y = 3.103 in.)	
12	129.0	1548	258.0	3.464	1242	231.1
13-1/2	145.1	2204	326.5	3.897	1398	260.0
15	161.3	3023	403.1	4.330	1553	288.9
16-1/2	177.4	4024	487.8	4.763	1708	317.8
18	193.5	5225	580.5	5.196	1863	346.7
19-1/2	209.6	6642	681.3	5.629	2019	375.6
21	225.8	8296	790.1	6.062	2174	404.5
22-1/2	241.9	10200	907.0	6.495	2329	433.4
24	258.0	12380	1032	6.928	2485	462.3
25-1/2	274.1	14850	1165	7.361	2640	491.1
27	290.3	17630	1306	7.794	2795	520.0
28-1/2	306.4	20740	1455	8.227	2950	548.9
30	322.5	24190	1613	8.660	3106	577.8
31-1/2	338.6	28000	1778	9.093	3261	606.7
33	354.8	32190	1951	9.526	3416	635.6
34-1/2	370.9	36790	2133	9.959	3572	664.5
36	387.0	41800	2322	10.39	3727	693.4
37-1/2	403.1	47240	2520	10.83	3882	722.3
39	419.3	53140	2725	11.26	4037	751.2
40-1/2	435.4	59510	2939	11.69	4193	780.0
42	451.5	66370	3161	12.12	4348	808.9
43-1/2	467.6	73740	3390	12.56	4503	837.8
45	483.8	81630	3628	12.99	4659	866.7
46-1/2	499.9	90070	3874	13.42	4814	895.6
48	516.0	99070	4128	13.86	4969	924.5
49-1/2	532.1	108700	4390	14.29	5124	953.4
51	548.3	118800	4660	14.72	5280	982.3
52-1/2	564.4	129600	4938	15.16	5435	1011
54	580.5	141100	5225	15.59	5590	1040
55-1/2	596.6	153100	5519	16.02	5746	1069
57	612.8	165900	5821	16.45	5901	1098
58-1/2	628.9	179300	6132	16.89	6056	1127
60	645.0	193500	6450	17.32	6211	1156

Table 1C Section Properties of *Western Species* Structural Glued Laminated Timber (Cont.)

Depth d (in.)	Area A (in.²)	X-X Axis			Y-Y Axis	
		I_x (in.⁴)	S_x (in.³)	r_x (in.)	I_y (in.⁴)	S_y (in.³)
		12-1/4 in. Width			**(r_y = 3.536 in.)**	
13-1/2	165.4	2512	372.1	3.897	2068	337.6
15	183.8	3445	459.4	4.330	2298	375.2
16-1/2	202.1	4586	555.8	4.763	2528	412.7
18	220.5	5954	661.5	5.196	2757	450.2
19-1/2	238.9	7569	776.3	5.629	2987	487.7
21	257.3	9454	900.4	6.062	3217	525.2
22-1/2	275.6	11630	1034	6.495	3447	562.7
24	294.0	14110	1176	6.928	3677	600.3
25-1/2	312.4	16930	1328	7.361	3906	637.8
27	330.8	20090	1488	7.794	4136	675.3
28-1/2	349.1	23630	1658	8.227	4366	712.8
30	367.5	27560	1838	8.660	4596	750.3
31-1/2	385.9	31910	2026	9.093	4825	787.8
33	404.3	36690	2223	9.526	5055	825.3
34-1/2	422.6	41920	2430	9.959	5285	862.9
36	441.0	47630	2646	10.39	5515	900.4
37-1/2	459.4	53830	2871	10.83	5745	937.9
39	477.8	60550	3105	11.26	5974	975.4
40-1/2	496.1	67810	3349	11.69	6204	1013
42	514.5	75630	3602	12.12	6434	1050
43-1/2	532.9	84030	3863	12.56	6664	1088
45	551.3	93020	4134	12.99	6893	1125
46-1/2	569.6	102600	4415	13.42	7123	1163
48	588.0	112900	4704	13.86	7353	1201
49-1/2	606.4	123800	5003	14.29	7583	1238
51	624.8	135400	5310	14.72	7813	1276
52-1/2	643.1	147700	5627	15.16	8042	1313
54	661.5	160700	5954	15.59	8272	1351
55-1/2	679.9	174500	6289	16.02	8502	1388
57	698.3	189100	6633	16.45	8732	1426
58-1/2	716.6	204400	6987	16.89	8962	1463
60	735.0	220500	7350	17.32	9191	1501

3

SECTION PROPERTIES

Table 1D   Section Properties of *Southern Pine* Structural Glued Laminated Timber

Depth	Area	X-X Axis				Y-Y Axis	
d (in.)	A (in.^{2})	I_x (in.^{4})	S_x (in.^{3})	r_x (in.)		I_y (in.^{4})	S_y (in.^{3})
2-1/2 in. Width						**($r_y = 0.722$ in.)**	
5-1/2	13.75	34.66	12.60	1.588		7.161	5.729
6-7/8	17.19	67.70	19.69	1.985		8.952	7.161
8-1/4	20.63	117.0	28.36	2.382		10.74	8.594
9-5/8	24.06	185.8	38.60	2.778		12.53	10.03
11	27.50	277.3	50.42	3.175		14.32	11.46
12-3/8	30.94	394.8	63.81	3.572		16.11	12.89
13-3/4	34.38	541.6	78.78	3.969		17.90	14.32
15-1/8	37.81	720.9	95.32	4.366		19.69	15.76
16-1/2	41.25	935.9	113.4	4.763		21.48	17.19
17-7/8	44.69	1190	133.1	5.160		23.27	18.62
19-1/4	48.13	1486	154.4	5.557		25.07	20.05
20-5/8	51.56	1828	177.2	5.954		26.86	21.48
22	55.00	2218	201.7	6.351		28.65	22.92
23-3/8	58.44	2661	227.7	6.748		30.44	24.35
3 in. Width						**($r_y = 0.866$ in.)**	
5-1/2	16.50	41.59	15.13	1.588		12.38	8.250
6-7/8	20.63	81.24	23.63	1.985		15.47	10.31
8-1/4	24.75	140.4	34.03	2.382		18.56	12.38
9-5/8	28.88	222.9	46.32	2.778		21.66	14.44
11	33.00	332.8	60.50	3.175		24.75	16.50
12-3/8	37.13	473.8	76.57	3.572		27.84	18.56
13-3/4	41.25	649.9	94.53	3.969		30.94	20.63
15-1/8	45.38	865.0	114.4	4.366		34.03	22.69
16-1/2	49.50	1123	136.1	4.763		37.13	24.75
17-7/8	53.63	1428	159.8	5.160		40.22	26.81
19-1/4	57.75	1783	185.3	5.557		43.31	28.88
20-5/8	61.88	2193	212.7	5.954		46.41	30.94
22	66.00	2662	242.0	6.351		49.50	33.00
23-3/8	70.13	3193	273.2	6.748		52.59	35.06
3-1/8 in. Width						**($r_y = 0.902$ in.)**	
5-1/2	17.19	43.33	15.76	1.588		13.99	8.952
6-7/8	21.48	84.62	24.62	1.985		17.48	11.19
8-1/4	25.78	146.2	35.45	2.382		20.98	13.43
9-5/8	30.08	232.2	48.25	2.778		24.48	15.67
11	34.38	346.6	63.02	3.175		27.97	17.90
12-3/8	38.67	493.5	79.76	3.572		31.47	20.14
13-3/4	42.97	677.0	98.47	3.969		34.97	22.38
15-1/8	47.27	901.1	119.1	4.366		38.46	24.62
16-1/2	51.56	1170	141.8	4.763		41.96	26.86
17-7/8	55.86	1487	166.4	5.160		45.46	29.09
19-1/4	60.16	1858	193.0	5.557		48.96	31.33
20-5/8	64.45	2285	221.6	5.954		52.45	33.57
22	68.75	2773	252.1	6.351		55.95	35.81
23-3/8	73.05	3326	284.6	6.748		59.45	38.05

Table 1D Section Properties of *Southern Pine* Structural Glued Laminated Timber (Cont.)

Depth	Area	X-X Axis			Y-Y Axis	
d (in.)	A (in.^{2})	I_x (in.^{4})	S_x (in.^{3})	r_x (in.)	I_y (in.^{4})	S_y (in.^{3})
3-1/2 in. Width					**(r_y = 1.010 in.)**	
5-1/2	19.25	48.53	17.65	1.588	19.65	11.23
6-7/8	24.06	94.78	27.57	1.985	24.56	14.04
8-1/4	28.88	163.8	39.70	2.382	29.48	16.84
9-5/8	33.69	260.1	54.04	2.778	34.39	19.65
11	38.50	388.2	70.58	3.175	39.30	22.46
12-3/8	43.31	552.7	89.33	3.572	44.21	25.27
13-3/4	48.13	758.2	110.3	3.969	49.13	28.07
15-1/8	52.94	1009	133.4	4.366	54.04	30.88
16-1/2	57.75	1310	158.8	4.763	58.95	33.69
17-7/8	62.56	1666	186.4	5.160	63.87	36.49
19-1/4	67.38	2081	216.2	5.557	68.78	39.30
20-5/8	72.19	2559	248.1	5.954	73.69	42.11
22	77.00	3106	282.3	6.351	78.60	44.92
23-3/8	81.81	3725	318.7	6.748	83.52	47.72
5 in. Width					**(r_y = 1.443 in.)**	
6-7/8	34.38	135.4	39.39	1.985	71.61	28.65
8-1/4	41.25	234.0	56.72	2.382	85.94	34.38
9-5/8	48.13	371.5	77.20	2.778	100.3	40.10
11	55.00	554.6	100.8	3.175	114.6	45.83
12-3/8	61.88	789.6	127.6	3.572	128.9	51.56
13-3/4	68.75	1083	157.6	3.969	143.2	57.29
15-1/8	75.63	1442	190.6	4.366	157.6	63.02
16-1/2	82.50	1872	226.9	4.763	171.9	68.75
17-7/8	89.38	2380	266.3	5.160	186.2	74.48
19-1/4	96.25	2972	308.8	5.557	200.5	80.21
20-5/8	103.1	3656	354.5	5.954	214.8	85.94
22	110.0	4437	403.3	6.351	229.2	91.67
23-3/8	116.9	5322	455.3	6.748	243.5	97.40
24-3/4	123.8	6317	510.5	7.145	257.8	103.1
26-1/8	130.6	7429	568.8	7.542	272.1	108.9
27-1/2	137.5	8665	630.2	7.939	286.5	114.6
28-7/8	144.4	10030	694.8	8.335	300.8	120.3
30-1/4	151.3	11530	762.6	8.732	315.1	126.0
31-5/8	158.1	13180	833.5	9.129	329.4	131.8
33	165.0	14970	907.5	9.526	343.8	137.5
34-3/8	171.9	16920	984.7	9.923	358.1	143.2
35-3/4	178.8	19040	1065	10.32	372.4	149.0

Depth	Area	X-X Axis			Y-Y Axis	
d (in.)	A (in.^{2})	I$_x$ (in.^{4})	S$_x$ (in.^{3})	r$_x$ (in.)	I$_y$ (in.^{4})	S$_y$ (in.^{3})
5-1/8 in. Width					(r$_y$ = 1.479 in.)	
6-7/8	35.23	138.8	40.37	1.985	77.12	30.10
8-1/4	42.28	239.8	58.14	2.382	92.55	36.12
9-5/8	49.33	380.8	79.13	2.778	108.0	42.13
11	56.38	568.4	103.4	3.175	123.4	48.15
12-3/8	63.42	809.4	130.8	3.572	138.8	54.17
13-3/4	70.47	1110	161.5	3.969	154.2	60.19
15-1/8	77.52	1478	195.4	4.366	169.7	66.21
16-1/2	84.56	1919	232.5	4.763	185.1	72.23
17-7/8	91.61	2439	272.9	5.160	200.5	78.25
19-1/4	98.66	3047	316.5	5.557	215.9	84.27
20-5/8	105.7	3747	363.4	5.954	231.4	90.29
22	112.8	4548	413.4	6.351	246.8	96.31
23-3/8	119.8	5455	466.7	6.748	262.2	102.3
24-3/4	126.8	6475	523.2	7.145	277.6	108.3
26-1/8	133.9	7615	583.0	7.542	293.1	114.4
27-1/2	140.9	8882	646	7.939	308.5	120.4
28-7/8	148.0	10280	712.2	8.335	323.9	126.4
30-1/4	155.0	11820	781.6	8.732	339.3	132.4
31-5/8	162.1	13510	854.3	9.129	354.8	138.4
33	169.1	15350	930.2	9.526	370.2	144.5
34-3/8	176.2	17350	1009	9.923	385.6	150.5
35-3/4	183.2	19510	1092	10.32	401.0	156.5
5-1/2 in. Width					(r$_y$ = 1.588 in.)	
6-7/8	37.81	148.9	43.33	1.985	95.32	34.66
8-1/4	45.38	257.4	62.39	2.382	114.4	41.59
9-5/8	52.94	408.7	84.92	2.778	133.4	48.53
11	60.50	610.0	110.9	3.175	152.5	55.46
12-3/8	68.06	868.6	140.4	3.572	171.6	62.39
13-3/4	75.63	1191	173.3	3.969	190.6	69.32
15-1/8	83.19	1586	209.7	4.366	209.7	76.26
16-1/2	90.75	2059	249.6	4.763	228.8	83.19
17-7/8	98.31	2618	292.9	5.160	247.8	90.12
19-1/4	105.9	3269	339.7	5.557	266.9	97.05
20-5/8	113.4	4021	389.9	5.954	286.0	104.0
22	121.0	4880	443.7	6.351	305.0	110.9
23-3/8	128.6	5854	500.9	6.748	324.1	117.8
24-3/4	136.1	6949	561.5	7.145	343.1	124.8
26-1/8	143.7	8172	625.6	7.542	362.2	131.7
27-1/2	151.3	9532	693.2	7.939	381.3	138.6
28-7/8	158.8	11030	764.3	8.335	400.3	145.6
30-1/4	166.4	12690	838.8	8.732	419.4	152.5
31-5/8	173.9	14500	916.8	9.129	438.5	159.4
33	181.5	16470	998.3	9.526	457.5	166.4
34-3/8	189.1	18620	1083	9.923	476.6	173.3
35-3/4	196.6	20940	1172	10.32	495.7	180.2

Table 1D   Section Properties of *Southern Pine* Structural Glued Laminated Timber (Cont.)

Depth	Area	X-X Axis			Y-Y Axis	
d (in.)	A (in.^{2})	I$_x$ (in.^{4})	S$_x$ (in.^{3})	r$_x$ (in.)	I$_y$ (in.^{4})	S$_y$ (in.^{3})
6-3/4 in. Width					**(r$_y$ = 1.949 in.)**	
6-7/8	46.41	182.8	53.17	1.985	176.2	52.21
8-1/4	55.69	315.9	76.57	2.382	211.4	62.65
9-5/8	64.97	501.6	104.2	2.778	246.7	73.09
11	74.25	748.7	136.1	3.175	281.9	83.53
12-3/8	83.53	1066	172.3	3.572	317.2	93.97
13-3/4	92.81	1462	212.7	3.969	352.4	104.4
15-1/8	102.1	1946	257.4	4.366	387.6	114.9
16-1/2	111.4	2527	306.3	4.763	422.9	125.3
17-7/8	120.7	3213	359.5	5.160	458.1	135.7
19-1/4	129.9	4012	416.9	5.557	493.4	146.2
20-5/8	139.2	4935	478.6	5.954	528.6	156.6
22	148.5	5990	544.5	6.351	563.8	167.1
23-3/8	157.8	7184	614.7	6.748	599.1	177.5
24-3/4	167.1	8528	689.1	7.145	634.3	187.9
26-1/8	176.3	10030	767.8	7.542	669.6	198.4
27-1/2	185.6	11700	850.8	7.939	704.8	208.8
28-7/8	194.9	13540	938.0	8.335	740.0	219.3
30-1/4	204.2	15570	1029	8.732	775.3	229.7
31-5/8	213.5	17790	1125	9.129	810.5	240.2
33	222.8	20210	1225	9.526	845.8	250.6
34-3/8	232.0	22850	1329	9.923	881.0	261.0
35-3/4	241.3	25700	1438	10.32	916.2	271.5
37-1/8	250.6	28780	1551	10.72	951.5	281.9
38-1/2	259.9	32100	1668	11.11	986.7	292.4
39-7/8	269.2	35660	1789	11.51	1022	302.8
41-1/4	278.4	39480	1914	11.91	1057	313.2
42-5/8	287.7	43560	2044	12.30	1092	323.7
44	297.0	47920	2178	12.70	1128	334.1
45-3/8	306.3	52550	2316	13.10	1163	344.6
46-3/4	315.6	57470	2459	13.50	1198	355.0
48-1/8	324.8	62700	2606	13.89	1233	365.4
49-1/2	334.1	68220	2757	14.29	1269	375.9
50-7/8	343.4	74070	2912	14.69	1304	386.3
52-1/4	352.7	80240	3071	15.08	1339	396.8
53-5/8	362.0	86740	3235	15.48	1374	407.2
55	371.3	93590	3403	15.88	1410	417.7
56-3/8	380.5	100800	3575	16.27	1445	428.1
57-3/4	389.8	108300	3752	16.67	1480	438.5
59-1/8	399.1	116300	3933	17.07	1515	449.0
60-1/2	408.4	124600	4118	17.46	1551	459.4

3

SECTION PROPERTIES

Table 1D Section Properties of *Southern Pine* Structural Glued Laminated Timber (Cont.)

Depth	Area	X-X Axis			Y-Y Axis	
d (in.)	A (in.^{2})	I_x (in.^{4})	S_x (in.^{3})	r_x (in.)	I_y (in.^{4})	S_y (in.^{3})
		8-1/2 in. Width			**(r_y = 2.454 in.)**	
9-5/8	81.81	631.6	131.2	2.778	492.6	115.9
11	93.50	942.8	171.4	3.175	562.9	132.5
12-3/8	105.2	1342	216.9	3.572	633.3	149.0
13-3/4	116.9	1841	267.8	3.969	703.7	165.6
15-1/8	128.6	2451	324.1	4.366	774.1	182.1
16-1/2	140.3	3182	385.7	4.763	844.4	198.7
17-7/8	151.9	4046	452.6	5.160	914.8	215.2
19-1/4	163.6	5053	525.0	5.557	985.2	231.8
20-5/8	175.3	6215	602.6	5.954	1056	248.4
22	187.0	7542	685.7	6.351	1126	264.9
23-3/8	198.7	9047	774.1	6.748	1196	281.5
24-3/4	210.4	10740	867.8	7.145	1267	298.0
26-1/8	222.1	12630	966.9	7.542	1337	314.6
27-1/2	233.8	14730	1071	7.939	1407	331.1
28-7/8	245.4	17050	1181	8.335	1478	347.7
30-1/4	257.1	19610	1296	8.732	1548	364.3
31-5/8	268.8	22400	1417	9.129	1618	380.8
33	280.5	25460	1543	9.526	1689	397.4
34-3/8	292.2	28770	1674	9.923	1759	413.9
35-3/4	303.9	32360	1811	10.32	1830	430.5
37-1/8	315.6	36240	1953	10.72	1900	447.0
38-1/2	327.3	40420	2100	11.11	1970	463.6
39-7/8	338.9	44910	2253	11.51	2041	480.2
41-1/4	350.6	49720	2411	11.91	2111	496.7
42-5/8	362.3	54860	2574	12.30	2181	513.3
44	374.0	60340	2743	12.70	2252	529.8
45-3/8	385.7	66170	2917	13.10	2322	546.4
46-3/4	397.4	72370	3096	13.50	2393	562.9
48-1/8	409.1	78950	3281	13.89	2463	579.5
49-1/2	420.8	85910	3471	14.29	2533	596.1
50-7/8	432.4	93270	3667	14.69	2604	612.6
52-1/4	444.1	101000	3868	15.08	2674	629.2
53-5/8	455.8	109200	4074	15.48	2744	645.7
55	467.5	117800	4285	15.88	2815	662.3
56-3/8	479.2	126900	4502	16.27	2885	678.8
57-3/4	490.9	136400	4725	16.67	2955	695.4
59-1/8	502.6	146400	4952	17.07	3026	712.0
60-1/2	514.3	156900	5185	17.46	3096	728.5

Table 1D Section Properties of *Southern Pine* Structural Glued Laminated Timber (Cont.)

Depth d (in.)	Area A (in.^{2})	X-X Axis			Y-Y Axis	
		I_x (in.^{4})	S_x (in.^{3})	r_x (in.)	I_y (in.^{4})	S_y (in.^{3})
10-1/2 in. Width					**(r_y = 3.031 in.)**	
11	115.5	1165	211.8	3.175	1061	202.1
12-3/8	129.9	1658	268.0	3.572	1194	227.4
13-3/4	144.4	2275	330.9	3.969	1326	252.7
15-1/8	158.8	3028	400.3	4.366	1459	277.9
16-1/2	173.3	3931	476.4	4.763	1592	303.2
17-7/8	187.7	4997	559.2	5.160	1724	328.5
19-1/4	202.1	6242	648.5	5.557	1857	353.7
20-5/8	216.6	7677	744.4	5.954	1990	379.0
22	231.0	9317	847.0	6.351	2122	404.3
23-3/8	245.4	11180	956.2	6.748	2255	429.5
24-3/4	259.9	13270	1072	7.145	2388	454.8
26-1/8	274.3	15600	1194	7.542	2520	480.0
27-1/2	288.8	18200	1323	7.939	2653	505.3
28-7/8	303.2	21070	1459	8.335	2786	530.6
30-1/4	317.6	24220	1601	8.732	2918	555.8
31-5/8	332.1	27680	1750	9.129	3051	581.1
33	346.5	31440	1906	9.526	3183	606.4
34-3/8	360.9	35540	2068	9.923	3316	631.6
35-3/4	375.4	39980	2237	10.32	3449	656.9
37-1/8	389.8	44770	2412	10.72	3581	682.2
38-1/2	404.3	49930	2594	11.11	3714	707.4
39-7/8	418.7	55480	2783	11.51	3847	732.7
41-1/4	433.1	61420	2978	11.91	3979	758.0
42-5/8	447.6	67760	3180	12.30	4112	783.2
44	462.0	74540	3388	12.70	4245	808.5
45-3/8	476.4	81740	3603	13.10	4377	833.8
46-3/4	490.9	89400	3825	13.50	4510	859.0
48-1/8	505.3	97530	4053	13.89	4643	884.3
49-1/2	519.8	106100	4288	14.29	4775	909.6
50-7/8	534.2	115200	4529	14.69	4908	934.8
52-1/4	548.6	124800	4778	15.08	5040	960.1
53-5/8	563.1	134900	5032	15.48	5173	985.4
55	577.5	145600	5294	15.88	5306	1011
56-3/8	591.9	156800	5562	16.27	5438	1036
57-3/4	606.4	168500	5836	16.67	5571	1061
59-1/8	620.8	180900	6118	17.07	5704	1086
60-1/2	635.3	193800	6405	17.46	5836	1112

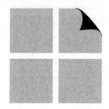

REFERENCE DESIGN VALUES

4

AMERICAN WOOD COUNCIL

Table 4A   Adjustment Factors

Repetitive Member Factor, C_r

Bending design values, F_b, for dimension lumber 2" to 4" thick shall be multiplied by the repetitive member factor, $C_r = 1.15$, when such members are used as joists, truss chords, rafters, studs, planks, decking, or similar members which are in contact or spaced not more than 24" on center, are not less than 3 in number and are joined by floor, roof, or other load distributing elements adequate to support the design load.

Wet Service Factor, C_M

When dimension lumber is used where moisture content will exceed 19% for an extended time period, design values shall be multiplied by the appropriate wet service factors from the following table:

Wet Service Factors, C_M

F_b	F_t	F_v	$F_{c\perp}$	F_c	E and E_{min}
0.85*	1.0	0.97	0.67	0.8**	0.9

* when $(F_b)(C_F) \leq 1,150$ psi, $C_M = 1.0$
** when $(F_c)(C_F) \leq 750$ psi, $C_M = 1.0$

Flat Use Factor, C_{fu}

Bending design values adjusted by size factors are based on edgewise use (load applied to narrow face). When dimension lumber is used flatwise (load applied to wide face), the bending design value, F_b, shall also be multiplied by the following flat use factors:

Flat Use Factors, C_{fu}

Width	Thickness (breadth)	
(depth)	2" & 3"	4"
2" & 3"	1.0	—
4"	1.1	1.0
5"	1.1	1.05
6"	1.15	1.05
8"	1.15	1.05
10" & wider	1.2	1.1

NOTE

To facilitate the use of Table 4A, shading has been employed to distinguish design values based on a 4" nominal width (Construction, Standard, and Utility grades) or a 6" nominal width (Stud grade) from design values based on a 12" nominal width (Select Structural, No.1 & Btr, No.1, No.2, and No.3 grades).

Size Factor, C_F

Tabulated bending, tension, and compression parallel to grain design values for dimension lumber 2" to 4" thick shall be multiplied by the following size factors:

Size Factors, C_F

Grades	Width (depth)	F_b Thickness (breadth) 2" & 3"	F_b Thickness (breadth) 4"	F_t	F_c
Select Structural, No.1 & Btr, No.1, No.2, No.3	2", 3", & 4"	1.5	1.5	1.5	1.15
	5"	1.4	1.4	1.4	1.1
	6"	1.3	1.3	1.3	1.1
	8"	1.2	1.3	1.2	1.05
	10"	1.1	1.2	1.1	1.0
	12"	1.0	1.1	1.0	1.0
	14" & wider	0.9	1.0	0.9	0.9
Stud	2", 3", & 4"	1.1	1.1	1.1	1.05
	5" & 6"	1.0	1.0	1.0	1.0
	8" & wider	Use No.3 Grade tabulated design values and size factors			
Construction, Standard	2", 3", & 4"	1.0	1.0	1.0	1.0
Utility	4"	1.0	1.0	1.0	1.0
	2" & 3"	0.4	—	0.4	0.6

Table 4A Reference Design Values for Visually Graded Dimension Lumber (2" - 4" thick)[1,2,3]

(All species except Southern Pine — see Table 4B) (Tabulated design values are for normal load duration and dry service conditions. See NDS 4.3 for a comprehensive description of design value adjustment factors.)

USE WITH TABLE 4A ADJUSTMENT FACTORS

Species and commercial grade	Size classification	Bending F_b	Tension parallel to grain F_t	Shear parallel to grain F_v	Compression perpendicular to grain $F_{c\perp}$	Compression parallel to grain F_c	Modulus of Elasticity E	E_{min}	Specific Gravity[4] G	Grading Rules Agency
ALASKA CEDAR										
Select Structural		1,150	625	165	525	1,000	1,400,000	510,000		
No. 1	2" & wider	975	525	165	525	900	1,300,000	470,000		
No. 2		800	425	165	525	750	1,200,000	440,000		
No. 3		450	250	165	525	425	1,100,000	400,000		
Stud	2" & wider	625	350	165	525	475	1,100,000	400,000	0.47	WCLIB
Construction		900	500	165	525	950	1,200,000	440,000		
Standard	2" - 4" wide	500	275	165	525	775	1,100,000	400,000		
Utility		250	125	165	525	500	1,000,000	370,000		
ALASKA HEMLOCK										
Select Structural		1,300	825	185	440	1,200	1,700,000	620,000		
No. 1	2" & wider	900	550	185	440	1,100	1,600,000	580,000		
No. 2		825	475	185	440	1,050	1,500,000	550,000		
No. 3		475	275	185	440	600	1,400,000	510,000		
Stud	2" & wider	650	375	185	440	650	1,400,000	510,000	0.46	WWPA
Construction		950	550	185	440	1,250	1,400,000	510,000		
Standard	2" - 4" wide	525	300	185	440	1,050	1,300,000	470,000		
Utility		250	150	185	440	700	1,200,000	440,000		
ALASKA SPRUCE										
Select Structural		1,400	900	160	330	1,200	1,600,000	580,000		
No. 1	2" & wider	950	600	160	330	1,100	1,500,000	550,000		
No. 2		875	500	160	330	1,050	1,400,000	510,000		
No. 3		500	300	160	330	600	1,300,000	470,000		
Stud	2" & wider	675	400	160	330	675	1,300,000	470,000	0.41	WWPA
Construction		1,000	575	160	330	1,250	1,300,000	470,000		
Standard	2" - 4" wide	550	325	160	330	1,050	1,200,000	440,000		
Utility		275	150	160	330	700	1,100,000	400,000		
ALASKA YELLOW CEDAR										
Select Structural		1,350	800	225	510	1,200	1,500,000	550,000		
No. 1	2" & wider	900	525	225	510	1,050	1,400,000	510,000		
No. 2		800	450	225	510	1,000	1,300,000	470,000		
No. 3		475	250	225	510	575	1,200,000	440,000		
Stud	2" & wider	625	350	225	510	625	1,200,000	440,000	0.46	WCLIB WWPA
Construction		925	500	225	510	1,250	1,300,000	470,000		
Standard	2" - 4" wide	500	275	225	510	1,050	1,100,000	400,000		
Utility		250	125	225	510	675	1,100,000	400,000		
ASPEN										
Select Structural		875	500	120	265	725	1,100,000	400,000		
No. 1	2" & wider	625	375	120	265	600	1,100,000	400,000		
No. 2		600	350	120	265	450	1,000,000	370,000		
No. 3		350	200	120	265	275	900,000	330,000		
Stud	2" & wider	475	275	120	265	300	900,000	330,000	0.39	NELMA NSLB WWPA
Construction		700	400	120	265	625	900,000	330,000		
Standard	2" - 4" wide	375	225	120	265	475	900,000	330,000		
Utility		175	100	120	265	300	800,000	290,000		
BALDCYPRESS										
Select Structural		1,200	650	160	615	1,200	1,400,000	510,000		
No. 1	2" & wider	1,000	550	160	615	1,050	1,400,000	510,000		
No. 2		825	450	160	615	900	1,300,000	470,000		
No. 3		475	250	160	615	525	1,200,000	440,000		
Stud	2" & wider	650	350	160	615	575	1,200,000	440,000	0.47	SPIB
Construction		925	500	160	615	1,100	1,200,000	440,000		
Standard	2" - 4" wide	525	275	160	615	925	1,100,000	400,000		
Utility		250	125	160	615	600	1,000,000	370,000		

Table 4A (Cont.) Reference Design Values for Visually Graded Dimension Lumber (2" – 4" thick)[1,2,3]

(All species except Southern Pine — see Table 4B) (Tabulated design values are for normal load duration and dry service conditions. See NDS 4.3 for a comprehensive description of design value adjustment factors.)

USE WITH TABLE 4A ADJUSTMENT FACTORS

| Species and commercial grade | Size classification | Design values in pounds per square inch (psi) | | | | | | | Specific Gravity[4] | Grading Rules Agency |
		Bending F_b	Tension parallel to grain F_t	Shear parallel to grain F_v	Compression perpendicular to grain $F_{c\perp}$	Compression parallel to grain F_c	Modulus of Elasticity E	Modulus of Elasticity E_{min}	G	
BEECH-BIRCH-HICKORY										
Select Structural	2" & wider	1,450	850	195	715	1,200	1,700,000	620,000	0.71	NELMA
No. 1		1,050	600	195	715	950	1,600,000	580,000		
No. 2		1,000	600	195	715	750	1,500,000	550,000		
No. 3		575	350	195	715	425	1,300,000	470,000		
Stud	2" & wider	775	450	195	715	475	1,300,000	470,000		
Construction		1,150	675	195	715	1,000	1,400,000	510,000		
Standard	2" - 4" wide	650	375	195	715	775	1,300,000	470,000		
Utility		300	175	195	715	500	1,200,000	440,000		
COAST SITKA SPRUCE										
Select Structural	2" & wider	1300	950	125	455	1200	1,700,000	620,000	0.43	NLGA
No. 1/ No. 2		925	550	125	455	1100	1,500,000	550,000		
No. 3		525	325	125	455	625	1,400,000	510,000		
Stud	2" & wider	725	450	125	455	675	1,400,000	510,000		
Construction		1050	650	125	455	1300	1,400,000	510,000		
Standard	2" - 4" wide	600	350	125	455	1100	1,300,000	470,000		
Utility		275	175	125	455	725	1,200,000	440,000		
COTTONWOOD										
Select Structural	2" & wider	875	525	125	320	775	1,200,000	440,000	0.41	NSLB
No. 1		625	375	125	320	625	1,200,000	440,000		
No. 2		625	350	125	320	475	1,100,000	400,000		
No. 3		350	200	125	320	275	1,000,000	370,000		
Stud	2" & wider	475	275	125	320	300	1,000,000	370,000		
Construction		700	400	125	320	650	1,000,000	370,000		
Standard	2" - 4" wide	400	225	125	320	500	900,000	330,000		
Utility		175	100	125	320	325	900,000	330,000		
DOUGLAS FIR-LARCH										
Select Structural	2" & wider	1,500	1,000	180	625	1,700	1,900,000	690,000	0.50	WCLIB WWPA
No. 1 & Btr		1,200	800	180	625	1,550	1,800,000	660,000		
No. 1		1,000	675	180	625	1,500	1,700,000	620,000		
No. 2		900	575	180	625	1,350	1,600,000	580,000		
No. 3		525	325	180	625	775	1,400,000	510,000		
Stud	2" & wider	700	450	180	625	850	1,400,000	510,000		
Construction		1,000	650	180	625	1,650	1,500,000	550,000		
Standard	2" - 4" wide	575	375	180	625	1,400	1,400,000	510,000		
Utility		275	175	180	625	900	1,300,000	470,000		
DOUGLAS FIR-LARCH (NORTH)										
Select Structural	2" & wider	1,350	825	180	625	1,900	1,900,000	690,000	0.49	NLGA
No. 1 & Btr		1,150	750	180	625	1,800	1,800,000	660,000		
No. 1/ No. 2		850	500	180	625	1,400	1,600,000	580,000		
No. 3		475	300	180	625	825	1,400,000	510,000		
Stud	2" & wider	650	400	180	625	900	1,400,000	510,000		
Construction		950	575	180	625	1,800	1,500,000	550,000		
Standard	2" - 4" wide	525	325	180	625	1,450	1,400,000	510,000		
Utility		250	150	180	625	950	1,300,000	470,000		
DOUGLAS FIR-SOUTH										
Select Structural	2" & wider	1,350	900	180	520	1,600	1,400,000	510,000	0.46	WWPA
No. 1		925	600	180	520	1,450	1,300,000	470,000		
No. 2		850	525	180	520	1,350	1,200,000	440,000		
No. 3		500	300	180	520	775	1,100,000	400,000		
Stud	2" & wider	675	425	180	520	850	1,100,000	400,000		
Construction		975	600	180	520	1,650	1,200,000	440,000		
Standard	2" - 4" wide	550	350	180	520	1,400	1,100,000	400,000		
Utility		250	150	180	520	900	1,000,000	370,000		

Table 4A (Cont.) Reference Design Values for Visually Graded Dimension Lumber (2" – 4" thick)[1,2,3]

(All species except Southern Pine—see Table 4B) (Tabulated design values are for normal load duration and dry service conditions. See NDS 4.3 for a comprehensive description of design value adjustment factors.)

USE WITH TABLE 4A ADJUSTMENT FACTORS

| Species and commercial grade | Size classification | Design values in pounds per square inch (psi) | | | | | | | Specific Gravity[4] | Grading Rules Agency |
		Bending F_b	Tension parallel to grain F_t	Shear parallel to grain F_v	Compression perpendicular to grain $F_{c\perp}$	Compression parallel to grain F_c	Modulus of Elasticity E	E_{min}	G	
EASTERN HEMLOCK-BALSAM FIR										
Select Structural		1,250	575	140	335	1,200	1,200,000	440,000		
No. 1	2" & wider	775	350	140	335	1,000	1,100,000	400,000		
No. 2		575	275	140	335	825	1,100,000	400,000		NELMA
No. 3		350	150	140	335	475	900,000	330,000	0.36	NSLB
Stud	2" & wider	450	200	140	335	525	900,000	330,000		
Construction		675	300	140	335	1,050	1,000,000	370,000		
Standard	2" - 4" wide	375	175	140	335	850	900,000	330,000		
Utility		175	75	140	335	550	800,000	290,000		
EASTERN HEMLOCK-TAMARACK										
Select Structural		1,250	575	170	555	1,200	1,200,000	440,000		
No. 1	2" & wider	775	350	170	555	1,000	1,100,000	400,000		
No. 2		575	275	170	555	825	1,100,000	400,000		NELMA
No. 3		350	150	170	555	475	900,000	330,000	0.41	NSLB
Stud	2" & wider	450	200	170	555	525	900,000	330,000		
Construction		675	300	170	555	1,050	1,000,000	370,000		
Standard	2" - 4" wide	375	175	170	555	850	900,000	330,000		
Utility		175	75	170	555	550	800,000	290,000		
EASTERN SOFTWOODS										
Select Structural		1,250	575	140	335	1,200	1,200,000	440,000		
No. 1	2" & wider	775	350	140	335	1,000	1,100,000	400,000		
No. 2		575	275	140	335	825	1,100,000	400,000		NELMA
No. 3		350	150	140	335	475	900,000	330,000	0.36	NSLB
Stud	2" & wider	450	200	140	335	525	900,000	330,000		
Construction		675	300	140	335	1,050	1,000,000	370,000		
Standard	2" - 4" wide	375	175	140	335	850	900,000	330,000		
Utility		175	75	140	335	550	800,000	290,000		
EASTERN WHITE PINE										
Select Structural		1,250	575	135	350	1,200	1,200,000	440,000		
No. 1	2" & wider	775	350	135	350	1,000	1,100,000	400,000		
No. 2		575	275	135	350	825	1,100,000	400,000		NELMA
No. 3		350	150	135	350	475	900,000	330,000	0.36	NSLB
Stud	2" & wider	450	200	135	350	525	900,000	330,000		
Construction		675	300	135	350	1,050	1,000,000	370,000		
Standard	2" - 4" wide	375	175	135	350	850	900,000	330,000		
Utility		175	75	135	350	550	800,000	290,000		
HEM-FIR										
Select Structural		1,400	925	150	405	1,500	1,600,000	580,000		
No. 1 & Btr		1,100	725	150	405	1,350	1,500,000	550,000		
No. 1	2" & wider	975	625	150	405	1,350	1,500,000	550,000		
No. 2		850	525	150	405	1,300	1,300,000	470,000		WCLIB
No. 3		500	300	150	405	725	1,200,000	440,000	0.43	WWPA
Stud	2" & wider	675	400	150	405	800	1,200,000	440,000		
Construction		975	600	150	405	1,550	1,300,000	470,000		
Standard	2" - 4" wide	550	325	150	405	1,300	1,200,000	440,000		
Utility		250	150	150	405	850	1,100,000	400,000		
HEM-FIR (NORTH)										
Select Structural		1,300	775	145	405	1,700	1,700,000	620,000		
No. 1 & Btr		1,200	725	145	405	1,550	1,700,000	620,000		
No. 1/ No. 2	2" & wider	1,000	575	145	405	1,450	1,600,000	580,000		
No. 3		575	325	145	405	850	1,400,000	510,000	0.46	NLGA
Stud	2" & wider	775	450	145	405	925	1,400,000	510,000		
Construction		1,150	650	145	405	1,750	1,500,000	550,000		
Standard	2" - 4" wide	650	350	145	405	1,500	1,400,000	510,000		
Utility		300	175	145	405	975	1,300,000	470,000		

4

REFERENCE DESIGN VALUES

(All species except Southern Pine—see Table 4B) (Tabulated design values are for normal load duration and dry service conditions. See NDS 4.3 for a comprehensive description of design value adjustment factors.)

USE WITH TABLE 4A ADJUSTMENT FACTORS

Species and commercial grade	Size classification	Design values in pounds per square inch (psi)							Specific Gravity[4]	Grading Rules Agency
		Bending F_b	Tension parallel to grain F_t	Shear parallel to grain F_v	Compression perpendicular to grain $F_{c\perp}$	Compression parallel to grain F_c	Modulus of Elasticity			
							E	E_{min}	G	
MIXED MAPLE										
Select Structural	2" & wider	1,000	600	195	620	875	1,300,000	470,000	0.55	NELMA
No. 1		725	425	195	620	700	1,200,000	440,000		
No. 2		700	425	195	620	550	1,100,000	400,000		
No. 3		400	250	195	620	325	1,000,000	370,000		
Stud	2" & wider	550	325	195	620	350	1,000,000	370,000		
Construction	2" - 4" wide	800	475	195	620	725	1,100,000	400,000		
Standard		450	275	195	620	575	1,000,000	370,000		
Utility		225	125	195	620	375	900,000	330,000		
MIXED OAK										
Select Structural	2" & wider	1,150	675	170	800	1,000	1,100,000	400,000	0.68	NELMA
No. 1		825	500	170	800	825	1,000,000	370,000		
No. 2		800	475	170	800	625	900,000	330,000		
No. 3		475	275	170	800	375	800,000	290,000		
Stud	2" & wider	625	375	170	800	400	800,000	290,000		
Construction	2" - 4" wide	925	550	170	800	850	900,000	330,000		
Standard		525	300	170	800	650	800,000	290,000		
Utility		250	150	170	800	425	800,000	290,000		
NORTHERN RED OAK										
Select Structural	2" & wider	1,400	800	220	885	1,150	1,400,000	510,000	0.68	NELMA
No. 1		1,000	575	220	885	925	1,400,000	510,000		
No. 2		975	575	220	885	725	1,300,000	470,000		
No. 3		550	325	220	885	425	1,200,000	440,000		
Stud	2" & wider	750	450	220	885	450	1,200,000	440,000		
Construction	2" - 4" wide	1,100	650	220	885	975	1,200,000	440,000		
Standard		625	350	220	885	750	1,100,000	400,000		
Utility		300	175	220	885	500	1,000,000	370,000		
NORTHERN SPECIES										
Select Structural	2" & wider	975	425	110	350	1,100	1,100,000	400,000	0.35	NLGA
No. 1/ No. 2		625	275	110	350	850	1,100,000	400,000		
No. 3		350	150	110	350	500	1,000,000	370,000		
Stud	2" & wider	475	225	110	350	550	1,000,000	370,000		
Construction	2" - 4" wide	700	325	110	350	1,050	1,000,000	370,000		
Standard		400	175	110	350	875	900,000	330,000		
Utility		175	75	110	350	575	900,000	330,000		
NORTHERN WHITE CEDAR										
Select Structural	2" & wider	775	450	120	370	750	800,000	290,000	0.31	NELMA
No. 1		575	325	120	370	600	700,000	260,000		
No. 2		550	325	120	370	475	700,000	260,000		
No. 3		325	175	120	370	275	600,000	220,000		
Stud	2" & wider	425	250	120	370	300	600,000	220,000		
Construction	2" - 4" wide	625	375	120	370	625	700,000	260,000		
Standard		350	200	120	370	475	600,000	220,000		
Utility		175	100	120	370	325	600,000	220,000		
RED MAPLE										
Select Structural	2" & wider	1,300	750	210	615	1,100	1,700,000	620,000	0.58	NELMA
No. 1		925	550	210	615	900	1,600,000	580,000		
No. 2		900	525	210	615	700	1,500,000	550,000		
No. 3		525	300	210	615	400	1,300,000	470,000		
Stud	2" & wider	700	425	210	615	450	1,300,000	470,000		
Construction	2" - 4" wide	1,050	600	210	615	925	1,400,000	510,000		
Standard		575	325	210	615	725	1,300,000	470,000		
Utility		275	150	210	615	475	1,200,000	440,000		

Table 4A (Cont.) Reference Design Values for Visually Graded Dimension Lumber (2" – 4" thick)[1,2,3]

(All species except Southern Pine — see Table 4B) (Tabulated design values are for normal load duration and dry service conditions. See NDS 4.3 for a comprehensive description of design value adjustment factors.)

USE WITH TABLE 4A ADJUSTMENT FACTORS

Species and commercial grade	Size classification	Design values in pounds per square inch (psi)							Specific Gravity[4]	Grading Rules Agency
		Bending	Tension parallel to grain	Shear parallel to grain	Compression perpendicular to grain	Compression parallel to grain	Modulus of Elasticity			
		F_b	F_t	F_v	$F_{c\perp}$	F_c	E	E_{min}	G	
RED OAK										
Select Structural		1,150	675	170	820	1,000	1,400,000	510,000		
No. 1	2" & wider	825	500	170	820	825	1,300,000	470,000		
No. 2		800	475	170	820	625	1,200,000	440,000		
No. 3		475	275	170	820	375	1,100,000	400,000	0.67	NELMA
Stud	2" & wider	625	375	170	820	400	1,100,000	400,000		
Construction		925	550	170	820	850	1,200,000	440,000		
Standard	2" - 4" wide	525	300	170	820	650	1,100,000	400,000		
Utility		250	150	170	820	425	1,000,000	370,000		
REDWOOD										
Clear Structural		1,750	1,000	160	650	1,850	1,400,000	510,000	0.44	
Select Structural		1,350	800	160	650	1,500	1,400,000	510,000	0.44	
Select Structural, open grain		1,100	625	160	425	1,100	1,100,000	400,000	0.37	
No. 1		975	575	160	650	1,200	1,300,000	470,000	0.44	
No. 1, open grain	2" & wider	775	450	160	425	900	1,100,000	400,000	0.37	
No. 2		925	525	160	650	950	1,200,000	440,000	0.44	
No. 2, open grain		725	425	160	425	700	1,000,000	370,000	0.37	RIS
No. 3		525	300	160	650	550	1,100,000	400,000	0.44	
No. 3, open grain		425	250	160	425	400	900,000	330,000	0.37	
Stud	2" & wider	575	325	160	425	450	900,000	330,000	0.44	
Construction		825	475	160	425	925	900,000	330,000	0.44	
Standard	2" - 4" wide	450	275	160	425	725	900,000	330,000	0.44	
Utility		225	125	160	425	475	800,000	290,000	0.44	
SPRUCE-PINE-FIR										
Select Structural		1,250	700	135	425	1,400	1,500,000	550,000		
No. 1/ No. 2	2" & wider	875	450	135	425	1,150	1,400,000	510,000		
No. 3		500	250	135	425	650	1,200,000	440,000		
Stud	2" & wider	675	350	135	425	725	1,200,000	440,000	0.42	NLGA
Construction		1,000	500	135	425	1,400	1,300,000	470,000		
Standard	2" - 4" wide	550	275	135	425	1,150	1,200,000	440,000		
Utility		275	125	135	425	750	1,100,000	400,000		
SPRUCE-PINE-FIR (SOUTH)										
Select Structural		1,300	575	135	335	1,200	1,300,000	470,000		
No. 1		875	400	135	335	1,050	1,200,000	440,000		
No. 2	2" & wider	775	350	135	335	1,000	1,100,000	400,000		NELMA
No. 3		450	200	135	335	575	1,000,000	370,000		NSLB
Stud	2" & wider	600	275	135	335	625	1,000,000	370,000	0.36	WCLIB
Construction		875	400	135	335	1,200	1,000,000	370,000		WWPA
Standard	2" - 4" wide	500	225	135	335	1,000	900,000	330,000		
Utility		225	100	135	335	675	900,000	330,000		
WESTERN CEDARS										
Select Structural		1,000	600	155	425	1,000	1,100,000	400,000		
No. 1	2" & wider	725	425	155	425	825	1,000,000	370,000		
No. 2		700	425	155	425	650	1,000,000	370,000		
No. 3		400	250	155	425	375	900,000	330,000	0.36	WCLIB
Stud	2" & wider	550	325	155	425	400	900,000	330,000		WWPA
Construction		800	475	155	425	850	900,000	330,000		
Standard	2" - 4" wide	450	275	155	425	650	800,000	290,000		
Utility		225	125	155	425	425	800,000	290,000		

4

REFERENCE DESIGN VALUES

(All species except Southern Pine — see Table 4B) (Tabulated design values are for normal load duration and dry service conditions. See NDS 4.3 for a comprehensive description of design value adjustment factors.)

USE WITH TABLE 4A ADJUSTMENT FACTORS

Species and commercial grade	Size classification	Design values in pounds per square inch (psi)							Specific Gravity[4]	Grading Rules Agency
		Bending F_b	Tension parallel to grain F_t	Shear parallel to grain F_v	Compression perpendicular to grain $F_{c\perp}$	Compression parallel to grain F_c	Modulus of Elasticity E	E_{min}	G	
WESTERN WOODS										
Select Structural	2" & wider	900	400	135	335	1,050	1,200,000	440,000	0.36	WCLIB WWPA
No. 1		675	300	135	335	950	1,100,000	400,000		
No. 2		675	300	135	335	900	1,000,000	370,000		
No. 3		375	175	135	335	525	900,000	330,000		
Stud	2" & wider	525	225	135	335	575	900,000	330,000		
Construction	2" - 4" wide	775	350	135	335	1,100	1,000,000	370,000		
Standard		425	200	135	335	925	900,000	330,000		
Utility		200	100	135	335	600	800,000	290,000		
WHITE OAK										
Select Structural	2" & wider	1,200	700	220	800	1,100	1,100,000	400,000	0.73	NELMA
No. 1		875	500	220	800	900	1,000,000	370,000		
No. 2		850	500	220	800	700	900,000	330,000		
No. 3		475	275	220	800	400	800,000	290,000		
Stud	2" & wider	650	375	220	800	450	800,000	290,000		
Construction	2" - 4" wide	950	550	220	800	925	900,000	330,000		
Standard		525	325	220	800	725	800,000	290,000		
Utility		250	150	220	800	475	800,000	290,000		
YELLOW CEDAR										
Select Structural	2" & wider	1200	725	175	540	1200	1,600,000	580,000	0.46	NLGA
No. 1/ No. 2		800	475	175	540	1000	1,400,000	510,000		
No. 3		475	275	175	540	575	1,200,000	440,000		
Stud	2" & wider	625	375	175	540	650	1,200,000	440,000		
Construction	2" - 4" wide	925	550	175	540	1200	1,300,000	470,000		
Standard		525	300	175	540	1050	1,200,000	440,000		
Utility		250	150	175	540	675	1,100,000	400,000		
YELLOW POPLAR										
Select Structural	2" & wider	1,000	575	145	420	900	1,500,000	550,000	0.43	NSLB
No. 1		725	425	145	420	725	1,400,000	510,000		
No. 2		700	400	145	420	575	1,300,000	470,000		
No. 3		400	225	145	420	325	1,200,000	440,000		
Stud	2" & wider	550	325	145	420	350	1,200,000	440,000		
Construction	2" - 4" wide	800	475	145	420	750	1,300,000	470,000		
Standard		450	250	145	420	575	1,100,000	400,000		
Utility		200	125	145	420	375	1,100,000	400,000		

1. **LUMBER DIMENSIONS.** Tabulated design values are applicable to lumber that will be used under dry conditions such as in most covered structures. For 2" to 4" thick lumber the DRY dressed sizes shall be used (see Table 1A) regardless of the moisture content at the time of manufacture or use. In calculating design values, the natural gain in strength and stiffness that occurs as lumber dries has been taken into consideration as well as the reduction in size that occurs when unseasoned lumber shrinks. The gain in load carrying capacity due to increased strength and stiffness resulting from drying more than offsets the design effect of size reductions due to shrinkage.

2. **STRESS-RATED BOARDS.** Stress-rated boards of nominal 1", 1-¼" and 1-½" thickness, 2" and wider, of most species, are permitted to use the design values shown for Select Structural, No.1 & Btr, No.1, No.2, No.3, Stud, Construction, Standard, Utility, and Clear Structural grades as shown in the 2" to 4" thick categories herein, when graded in accordance with the stress-rated board provisions in the applicable grading rules. Information on stress-rated board grades applicable to the various species is available from the respective grading rules agencies. Information on additional design values may also be available from the respective grading rules agencies.

3. When individual species or species groups are combined, the design values to be used for the combination shall be the lowest design values for each individual species or species group for each design property.

4. Specific gravity, G, based on weight and volume when oven-dry.

Table 4B Adjustment Factors

Size Factor, C_F

Appropriate size adjustment factors have already been incorporated in the tabulated design values for most thicknesses of Southern Pine and Mixed Southern Pine dimension lumber. For dimension lumber 4" thick, 8" and wider (all grades except Dense Structural 86, Dense Structural 72, and Dense Structural 65), tabulated bending design values, F_b, shall be permitted to be multiplied by the size factor, $C_F = 1.1$. For dimension lumber wider than 12" (all grades except Dense Structural 86, Dense Structural 72, and Dense Structural 65), tabulated bending, tension and compression parallel to grain design values for 12" wide lumber shall be multiplied by the size factor, $C_F = 0.9$. When the depth, d, of Dense Structural 86, Dense Structural 72, or Dense Structural 65 dimension lumber exceeds 12", the tabulated bending design value, F_b, shall be multiplied by the following size factor:

$$C_F = (12/d)^{1/9}$$

Repetitive Member Factor, C_r

Bending design values, F_b, for dimension lumber 2" to 4" thick shall be multiplied by the repetitive member factor, $C_r = 1.15$, when such members are used as joists, truss chords, rafters, studs, planks, decking, or similar members which are in contact or spaced not more than 24" on center, are not less than 3 in number and are joined by floor, roof, or other load distributing elements adequate to support the design load.

Flat Use Factor, C_{fu}

Bending design values adjusted by size factors are based on edgewise use (load applied to narrow face). When dimension lumber is used flatwise (load applied to wide face), the bending design value, F_b, shall also be multiplied by the following flat use factors:

Flat Use Factors, C_{fu}

Width (depth)	Thickness (breadth)	
	2" & 3"	4"
2" & 3"	1.0	—
4"	1.1	1.0
5"	1.1	1.05
6"	1.15	1.05
8"	1.15	1.05
10" & wider	1.2	1.1

Wet Service Factor, C_M

When dimension lumber is used where moisture content will exceed 19% for an extended time period, design values shall be multiplied by the appropriate wet service factors from the following table (for surfaced dry Dense Structural 86, Dense Structural 72, and Dense Structural 65 use tabulated surfaced green design values for wet service conditions without further adjustment):

Wet Service Factors, C_M

F_b	F_t	F_v	$F_{c\perp}$	F_c	E and E_{min}
0.85*	1.0	0.97	0.67	0.8**	0.9

* when $(F_b)(C_F) \leq 1,150$ psi, $C_M = 1.0$

** when $(F_c) \leq 750$ psi, $C_M = 1.0$

Table 4B   Reference Design Values for Visually Graded Southern Pine Dimension Lumber (2" – 4" thick)[1,2,3,4,5]

(Tabulated design values are for normal load duration and dry service conditions, unless specified otherwise. See NDS 4.3 for a comprehensive description of design value adjustment factors.)

USE WITH TABLE 4B ADJUSTMENT FACTORS

Species and commercial grade	Size classification	Design values in pounds per square inch (psi)							Specific Gravity[6]	Grading Rules Agency
		Bending F_b	Tension parallel to grain F_t	Shear parallel to grain F_v	Compression perpendicular to grain $F_{c\perp}$	Compression parallel to grain F_c	Modulus of Elasticity		G	
							E	E_{min}		
SOUTHERN PINE										
Dense Select Structural	2" – 4" wide	3,050	1,650	175	660	2,250	1,900,000	690,000	0.55	
Select Structural		2,850	1,600	175	565	2,100	1,800,000	660,000		
Non-Dense Select Structural		2,650	1,350	175	480	1,950	1,700,000	620,000		
No.1 Dense		2,000	1,100	175	660	2,000	1,800,000	660,000		
No.1		1,850	1,050	175	565	1,850	1,700,000	620,000		
No.1 Non-Dense		1,700	900	175	480	1,700	1,600,000	580,000		
No.2 Dense		1,700	875	175	660	1,850	1,700,000	620,000		
No.2		1,500	825	175	565	1,650	1,600,000	580,000		
No.2 Non-Dense		1,350	775	175	480	1,600	1,400,000	510,000		
No.3 and Stud		850	475	175	565	975	1,400,000	510,000		
Construction	4" wide	1,100	625	175	565	1,800	1,500,000	550,000	0.55	
Standard		625	350	175	565	1,500	1,300,000	470,000		
Utility		300	175	175	565	975	1,300,000	470,000		
Dense Select Structural	5" – 6" wide	2,700	1,500	175	660	2,150	1,900,000	690,000	0.55	
Select Structural		2,550	1,400	175	565	2,000	1,800,000	660,000		
Non-Dense Select Structural		2,350	1,200	175	480	1,850	1,700,000	620,000		
No.1 Dense		1,750	950	175	660	1,900	1,800,000	660,000		
No.1		1,650	900	175	565	1,750	1,700,000	620,000		
No.1 Non-Dense		1,500	800	175	480	1,600	1,600,000	580,000		
No.2 Dense		1,450	775	175	660	1,750	1,700,000	620,000		
No.2		1,250	725	175	565	1,600	1,600,000	580,000		
No.2 Non-Dense		1,150	675	175	480	1,500	1,400,000	510,000		
No.3 and Stud		750	425	175	565	925	1,400,000	510,000		
Dense Select Structural	8" wide	2,450	1,350	175	660	2,050	1,900,000	690,000	0.55	SPIB
Select Structural		2,300	1,300	175	565	1,900	1,800,000	660,000		
Non-Dense Select Structural		2,100	1,100	175	480	1,750	1,700,000	620,000		
No.1 Dense		1,650	875	175	660	1,800	1,800,000	660,000		
No.1		1,500	825	175	565	1,650	1,700,000	620,000		
No.1 Non-Dense		1,350	725	175	480	1,550	1,600,000	580,000		
No.2 Dense		1,400	675	175	660	1,700	1,700,000	620,000		
No.2		1,200	650	175	565	1,550	1,600,000	580,000		
No.2 Non-Dense		1,100	600	175	480	1,450	1,400,000	510,000		
No.3 and Stud		700	400	175	565	875	1,400,000	510,000		
Dense Select Structural	10" wide	2,150	1,200	175	660	2,000	1,900,000	690,000	0.55	
Select Structural		2,050	1,100	175	565	1,850	1,800,000	660,000		
Non-Dense Select Structural		1,850	950	175	480	1,750	1,700,000	620,000		
No.1 Dense		1,450	775	175	660	1,750	1,800,000	660,000		
No.1		1,300	725	175	565	1,600	1,700,000	620,000		
No.1 Non-Dense		1,200	650	175	480	1,500	1,600,000	580,000		
No.2 Dense		1,200	625	175	660	1,650	1,700,000	620,000		
No.2		1,050	575	175	565	1,500	1,600,000	580,000		
No.2 Non-Dense		950	550	175	480	1,400	1,400,000	510,000		
No.3 and Stud		600	325	175	565	850	1,400,000	510,000		
Dense Select Structural	12" wide	2,050	1,100	175	660	1,950	1,900,000	690,000	0.55	
Select Structural		1,900	1,050	175	565	1,800	1,800,000	660,000		
Non-Dense Select Structural		1,750	900	175	480	1,700	1,700,000	620,000		
No.1 Dense		1,350	725	175	660	1,700	1,800,000	660,000		
No.1		1,250	675	175	565	1,600	1,700,000	620,000		
No.1 Non-Dense		1,150	600	175	480	1,500	1,600,000	580,000		
No.2 Dense		1,150	575	175	660	1,600	1,700,000	620,000		
No.2		975	550	175	565	1,450	1,600,000	580,000		
No.2 Non-Dense		900	525	175	480	1,350	1,400,000	510,000		
No.3 and Stud		575	325	175	565	825	1,400,000	510,000		

Table 4B (Cont.) Reference Design Values for Visually Graded Southern Pine Dimension Lumber (2" – 4" thick)[1,2,3,4,5]

(Tabulated design values are for normal load duration and dry service conditions, unless specified otherwise. See NDS 4.3 for a comprehensive description of design value adjustment factors.)

4

REFERENCE DESIGN VALUES

USE WITH TABLE 4B ADJUSTMENT FACTORS

Species and commercial grade	Size classification	Design values in pounds per square inch (psi)							Specific Gravity[6]	Grading Rules Agency
		Bending F_b	Tension parallel to grain F_t	Shear parallel to grain F_v	Compression perpendicular to grain $F_{c\perp}$	Compression parallel to grain F_c	Modulus of Elasticity		G	
							E	E_{min}		
SOUTHERN PINE		(Surfaced Dry - Used in dry service condtions - 19% or less moisture content)								
Dense Structural 86		2,600	1,750	175	660	2,000	1,800,000	660,000		
Dense Structural 72	2" & wider	2,200	1,450	175	660	1,650	1,800,000	660,000	0.55	SPIB
Dense Structural 65		2,000	1,300	175	660	1,500	1,800,000	660,000		
SOUTHERN PINE		(Surfaced Green - Used in any service condtion)								
Dense Structural 86		2,100	1,400	165	440	1,300	1,600,000	580,000		
Dense Structural 72	2-1/2" & wider	1,750	1,200	165	440	1,100	1,600,000	580,000	0.55	SPIB
Dense Structural 65	2-1/2"-4" thick	1,600	1,050	165	440	1,000	1,600,000	580,000		
MIXED SOUTHERN PINE										
Select Structural		2,050	1,200	175	565	1,800	1,600,000	580,000		
No.1	2" - 4" wide	1,450	875	175	565	1,650	1,500,000	550,000	0.51	
No.2		1,300	775	175	565	1,650	1,400,000	510,000		
No.3 and Stud		750	450	175	565	950	1,200,000	440,000		
Construction		1,000	600	175	565	1,700	1,300,000	470,000		
Standard	4" wide	550	325	175	565	1,450	1,200,000	440,000	0.51	
Utility		275	150	175	565	950	1,100,000	400,000		
Select Structural		1,850	1,100	175	565	1,700	1,600,000	580,000		
No.1	5" - 6" wide	1,300	750	175	565	1,550	1,500,000	550,000	0.51	
No.2		1,150	675	175	565	1,550	1,400,000	510,000		
No.3 and Stud		675	400	175	565	875	1,200,000	440,000		SPIB
Select Structural		1,750	1,000	175	565	1,600	1,600,000	580,000		
No.1	8" wide	1,200	700	175	565	1,450	1,500,000	550,000	0.51	
No.2		1,050	625	175	565	1,450	1,400,000	510,000		
No.3 and Stud		625	375	175	565	850	1,200,000	440,000		
Select Structural		1,500	875	175	565	1,600	1,600,000	580,000		
No.1	10" wide	1,050	600	175	565	1,450	1,500,000	550,000	0.51	
No.2		925	550	175	565	1,450	1,400,000	510,000		
No.3 and Stud		525	325	175	565	825	1,200,000	440,000		
Select Structural		1,400	825	175	565	1,550	1,600,000	580,000		
No.1	12" wide	975	575	175	565	1,400	1,500,000	550,000	0.51	
No.2		875	525	175	565	1,400	1,400,000	510,000		
No.3 and Stud		500	300	175	565	800	1,200,000	440,000		

1. **LUMBER DIMENSIONS.** Tabulated design values are applicable to lumber that will be used under dry conditions such as in most covered structures. For 2" to 4" thick lumber the DRY dressed sizes shall be used (see Table 1A) regardless of the moisture content at the time of manufacture or use. In calculating design values, the natural gain in strength and stiffness that occurs as lumber dries has been taken into consideration as well as the reduction in size that occurs when unseasoned lumber shrinks. The gain in load carrying capacity due to increased strength and stiffness resulting from drying more than offsets the design effect of size reductions due to shrinkage.

2. **STRESS-RATED BOARDS.** Information for various grades of Southern Pine stress-rated boards of nominal 1", 1-¼", and 1-½" thickness, 2" and wider is available from the Southern Pine Inspection Bureau (SPIB) in the *Standard Grading Rules for Southern Pine Lumber.*

3. **SPRUCE PINE.** To obtain recommended design values for Spruce Pine graded to SPIB rules, multiply the appropriate design values for Mixed Southern Pine by the corresponding conversion factor shown below and round to the nearest 100,000 psi for E; to the nearest 10,000 psi for E; to the next lower multiple of 5 psi for F_v and $F_{c\perp}$; to the next lower multiple of 50 psi for F_b, F_t, and F_c if 1,000 psi or greater, 25 psi otherwise.

CONVERSION FACTORS FOR DETERMINING DESIGN VALUES FOR SPRUCE PINE

	Bending F_b	Tension parallel to grain F_t	Shear parallel to grain F_v	Compression perpendicular to grain $F_{c\perp}$	Compression parallel to grain F_c	Modulus of Elasticity E and E_{min}
Conversion Factor	0.78	0.78	0.98	0.73	0.78	0.82

4. **SIZE FACTOR.** For sizes wider than 12", use size factors for F_b, F_t, and F_c specified for the 12" width. Use 100% of the F_v, $F_{c\perp}$, E, and E_{min} specified for the 12" width.

5. When individual species or species groups are combined, the design values to be used for the combination shall be the lowest design values for each individual species or species group for each design property.

6. Specific gravity, G, based on weight and volume when oven-dry.

Table 4C Adjustment Factors

Flat Use Factor, C_{fu}

Bending design values are based on edgewise use (load applied to narrow face). When dimension lumber is used flatwise (load applied to wide face), the bending design value, F_b, shall be multiplied by the following flat use factors:

Flat Use Factors, C_{fu}

Width (depth)	Thickness (breadth)
	2"
2" & 3"	1.0
4"	1.1
5"	1.1
6"	1.15
8"	1.15
10" & wider	1.2

Repetitive Member Factor, C_r

Bending design values, F_b, for dimension lumber 2" to 4" thick shall be multiplied by the repetitive member factor, $C_r = 1.15$, when such members are used as joists, truss chords, rafters, studs, planks, decking, or similar members which are in contact or spaced not more than 24" on center, are not less than 3 in number and are joined by floor, roof, or other load distributing elements adequate to support the design load.

Wet Service Factor, C_M

When dimension lumber is used where moisture content will exceed 19% for an extended time period, design values shall be multiplied by the appropriate wet service factors from the following table:

Wet Service Factors, C_M

F_b	F_t	F_v	$F_{c\perp}$	F_c	E and E_{min}
0.85*	1.0	0.97	0.67	0.8**	0.9

* when $F_b \leq 1,150$ psi, $C_M = 1.0$
** when $F_c \leq 750$ psi, $C_M = 1.0$

Table 4C Reference Design Values for Mechanically Graded Dimension Lumber[1,2,3]

(Tabulated design values are for normal load duration and dry service conditions, unless specified otherwise. See NDS 4.3 for a comprehensive description of design value adjustment factors.)

USE WITH TABLE 4C ADJUSTMENT FACTORS

Commercial grade	Size classification	Design values in pounds per square inch (psi)					Grading Rules Agency
		Bending F_b	Tension parallel to grain F_t	Compression parallel to grain F_c	Modulus of Elasticity E	E_{min}	
MACHINE STRESS RATED (MSR) LUMBER							
750f-1.4E		750	425	925	1,400,000	710,000	SPIB
850f-1.4E		850	475	975	1,400,000	710,000	SPIB
900f-1.0E		900	350	1,050	1,000,000	510,000	WCLIB, WWPA, NELMA, NSLB
975f-1.6E		975	550	1,450	1,600,000	810,000	SPIB
1050f-1.2E		1,050	450	1,225	1,200,000	610,000	SPIB
1050f-1.6E		1,050	575	1,500	1,600,000	810,000	SPIB
1200f-1.2E		1,200	600	1,400	1,200,000	610,000	NLGA, WCLIB, WWPA, NELMA, NSLB
1200f-1.3E		1,200	600	1,400	1,300,000	660,000	SPIB
1200f-1.6E		1,200	650	1,550	1,600,000	810,000	SPIB
1250f-1.4E		1,250	800	1,475	1,400,000	710,000	WCLIB
1250f-1.6E		1,250	725	1,600	1,600,000	810,000	SPIB
1350f-1.3E		1,350	750	1,600	1,300,000	660,000	NLGA, WCLIB, WWPA, NELMA, NSLB
1350f-1.4E		1,350	750	1,600	1,400,000	710,000	SPIB
1400f-1.2E		1,400	800	1,600	1,200,000	610,000	NLGA
1450f-1.3E		1,450	800	1,625	1,300,000	660,000	NLGA, WCLIB, WWPA, NELMA, NSLB
1450f-1.3E		1,450	825	1,600	1,300,000	660,000	SPIB
1450f-1.5E		1,450	875	1,625	1,500,000	760,000	WCLIB
1500f-1.4E		1,500	900	1,650	1,400,000	710,000	NLGA, WCLIB, WWPA, NELMA, NSLB
1500f-1.5E		1,500	900	1,650	1,500,000	760,000	SPIB
1500f-1.6E		1,500	900	1,650	1,600,000	810,000	SPIB
1500f-1.7E		1,500	900	1,650	1,700,000	860,000	SPIB
1600f-1.4E	2" and less in thickness	1,600	950	1,675	1,400,000	710,000	NLGA
1650f-1.3E		1,650	1,020	1,700	1,300,000	660,000	NLGA
1650f-1.5E		1,650	1,020	1,700	1,500,000	760,000	NLGA, SPIB, WCLIB, WWPA, NELMA, NSLB
1650f-1.6E	2" and wider	1,650	1,175	1,700	1,600,000	810,000	WCLIB
1650f-1.7E		1,650	1,020	1,750	1,700,000	860,000	SPIB
1700f-1.6E		1700	1,175	1,725	1,600,000	810,000	WCLIB
1800f-1.5E		1,800	1,300	1,750	1,500,000	760,000	NLGA
1800f-1.6E		1,800	1,175	1,750	1,600,000	810,000	NLGA, SPIB, WCLIB, WWPA, NELMA, NSLB
1800f-1.8E		1,800	1,200	1,750	1,800,000	910,000	WCLIB
1800f-2.0E		1,800	1,175	1,750	2,000,000	1,020,000	WCLIB
1850f-1.7E		1,850	1,175	1,850	1,700,000	860,000	SPIB
1950f-1.5E		1,950	1,375	1,800	1,500,000	760,000	SPIB
1950f-1.7E		1,950	1,375	1,800	1,700,000	860,000	NLGA, SPIB, WCLIB, WWPA, NELMA, NSLB
2000f-1.6E		2,000	1,300	1,825	1,600,000	810,000	NLGA
2100f-1.8E		2,100	1,575	1,875	1,800,000	910,000	NLGA, SPIB, WCLIB, WWPA, NELMA, NSLB
2250f-1.7E		2,250	1750	1,925	1,700,000	860,000	NLGA
2250f-1.8E		2,250	1750	1,925	1,800,000	910,000	NLGA, WCLIB
2250f-1.9E		2,250	1750	1,925	1,900,000	970,000	NLGA, SPIB, WCLIB, WWPA, NELMA, NSLB
2400f-1.8E		2,400	1925	1,975	1,800,000	910,000	NLGA
2400f-2.0E		2,400	1925	1,975	2,000,000	1,020,000	NLGA, SPIB, WCLIB, WWPA, NELMA, NSLB
2500f-2.2E		2,500	1750	2,000	2,200,000	1,120,000	WCLIB
2550f-1.8E		2,550	1400	2,000	1,800,000	910,000	SPIB
2550f-2.1E		2,550	2050	2,025	2,100,000	1,070,000	NLGA, SPIB, WCLIB, WWPA, NELMA, NSLB
2700f-2.0E		2,700	1800	2,100	2,000,000	1,020,000	WCLIB
2700f-2.2E		2,700	2150	2,100	2,200,000	1,120,000	NLGA, SPIB, WCLIB, WWPA, NELMA, NSLB
2850f-1.8E		2,850	1600	2,100	1,800,000	910,000	SPIB
2850f-2.3E		2,850	2300	2,150	2,300,000	1,170,000	NLGA, SPIB, WCLIB, WWPA, NELMA, NSLB
3000f-2.4E		3,000	2,400	2,200	2,400,000	1,220,000	NLGA, SPIB

4

REFERENCE DESIGN VALUES

Table 4C (Cont.)

Reference Design Values for Mechanically Graded Dimension Lumber[1,2,]

(Tabulated design values are for normal load duration and dry service conditions, unless specified otherwise. See NDS 4.3 for a comprehensive description of design value adjustment factors.)

USE WITH TABLE 4C ADJUSTMENT FACTORS

Commercial grade	Size classification	Design values in pounds per square inch (psi)					Grading Rules Agency
		Bending F_b	Tension parallel to grain F_t	Compression parallel to grain F_c	Modulus of Elasticity E	E_{min}	
MACHINE EVALUATED LUMBER (MEL)							
M-5		900	500	1,050	1,100,000	510,000	SPIB
M-6		1,100	600	1,300	1,000,000	470,000	SPIB
M-7		1,200	650	1,400	1,100,000	510,000	SPIB
M-8		1,300	700	1,500	1,300,000	610,000	SPIB
M-9		1,400	800	1,600	1,400,000	650,000	SPIB
M-10		1,400	800	1,600	1,200,000	560,000	NLGA, SPIB
M-11		1,550	850	1,675	1,500,000	700,000	NLGA, SPIB
M-12		1,600	850	1,675	1,600,000	750,000	NLGA, SPIB
M-13		1,600	950	1,675	1,400,000	650,000	NLGA, SPIB
M-14		1,800	1,000	1,750	1,700,000	790,000	NLGA, SPIB
M-15		1,800	1,100	1,750	1,500,000	700,000	NLGA, SPIB
M-16		1,800	1,300	1,750	1,500,000	700,000	SPIB
M-17[4]		1,950	1,300	2,050	1,700,000	790,000	SPIB
M-18	2" and less in thickness	2,000	1,200	1,825	1,800,000	840,000	NLGA, SPIB
M-19		2,000	1,300	1,825	1,600,000	750,000	NLGA, SPIB
M-20[4]		2,000	1,600	2,100	1,900,000	890,000	SPIB
M-21	2" and wider	2,300	1,400	1,950	1,900,000	890,000	NLGA, SPIB
M-22		2,350	1,500	1,950	1,700,000	790,000	NLGA, SPIB
M-23		2,400	1,900	1,975	1,800,000	840,000	NLGA, SPIB
M-24		2,700	1,800	2,100	1,900,000	890,000	NLGA, SPIB
M-25		2,750	2,000	2,100	2,200,000	1,030,000	NLGA, SPIB
M-26		2,800	1,800	2,150	2,000,000	930,000	NLGA, SPIB
M-27[4]		3,000	2,000	2,400	2,100,000	980,000	SPIB
M-28		2,200	1,600	1,900	1,700,000	790,000	SPIB
M-29		1,550	850	1,650	1,700,000	790,000	SPIB
M-30		2,050	1,050	1,850	1,700,000	790,000	SPIB
M-31		2,850	1,600	2,150	1,900,000	890,000	SPIB
M-32		750	425	925	1,400,000	650,000	SPIB
M-33		850	475	975	1,400,000	650,000	SPIB
M-34		975	550	1,450	1,600,000	750,000	SPIB
M-35		1,050	575	1,500	1,600,000	750,000	SPIB
M-36		1,200	650	1,550	1,600,000	750,000	SPIB
M-37		1,250	725	1,600	1,600,000	750,000	SPIB
M-38		1,500	900	1,650	1,600,000	750,000	SPIB
M-39		1,650	1,020	1,750	1,700,000	790,000	SPIB
M-40		1,850	1,175	1,850	1,700,000	790,000	SPIB

Table 4C Footnotes

1. **LUMBER DIMENSIONS.** Tabulated design values are applicable to lumber that will be used under dry conditions such as in most covered structures. For 2" to 4" thick lumber the DRY dressed sizes shall be used (see Table 1A) regardless of the moisture content at the time of manufacture or use. In calculating design values, the natural gain in strength and stiffness that occurs as lumber dries has been taken into consideration as well as the reduction in size that occurs when unseasoned lumber shrinks. The gain in load carrying capacity due to increased strength and stiffness resulting from drying more than offsets the design effect of size reductions due to shrinkage.

2. **SPECIFIC GRAVITY, G, SHEAR PARALLEL TO GRAIN, F_v, AND COMPRESSION PERPENDICULAR TO GRAIN, $F_{c\perp}$.** Values for specific gravity, G, shear parallel to grain, F_v, and compression perpendicular to grain, $F_{c\perp}$, are provided below for MSR and MEL lumber. For species or species groups not shown below, the G, F_v, and $F_{c\perp}$ values for visually graded lumber may be used. Higher G values may be claimed when (a) specifically assigned by the rules writing agency or (b) when qualified by test, quality controlled for G and provided for on the grade stamp. When a different G value is provided on the grade stamp, higher F_v and $F_{c\perp}$ design values may be calculated in accordance with the grading rule requirements.

Species	Modulus of Elasticity E (x10^6) psi	Specific Gravity G	Design values in pounds per square inch (psi)		Grading Rules Agency
			Shear parallel to grain F_v	Compression perpendicular to grain $F_{c\perp}$	
	1.0 and higher	0.50	180	625	WWPA
Douglas Fir-Larch	2.0	0.51	180	670	
	2.1	0.52	180	690	
	2.2	0.53	180	715	WWPA
	2.3	0.54	185	735	
	2.4	0.55	185	760	
	1.0 and higher	0.50	170	625	WCLIB
Douglas Fir-Larch	2.0	0.51	170	670	
	2.1	0.52	170	690	
	2.2	0.53	170	715	WCLIB
	2.3	0.54	170	735	
	2.4	0.55	170	760	
Douglas Fir-Larch (N)	1.2 to 1.9	0.49	180	625	NLGA
	2.0 to 2.2	0.53	180	715	
	2.3 & higher	0.57	190	715	NLGA
Douglas Fir-South	1.0 and higher	0.46	180	520	WWPA
Englemann Spruce-Lodgepole Pine	1.0 and higher	0.38	135	335	WWPA
	1.5 and higher	0.46	160	555	WWPA
	1.0 and higher	0.43	140	405	WCLIB
	1.0 and higher	0.43	150	405	WWPA
	1.6	0.44	155	510	
	1.7	0.45	160	535	
	1.8	0.46	160	555	
Hem-Fir	1.9	0.47	165	580	
	2.0	0.48	170	600	WCLIB, WWPA
	2.1	0.49	170	625	
	2.2	0.50	175	645	
	2.3	0.51	175	670	
	2.4	0.52	180	690	
Hem-Fir (N)	1.0 and higher	0.46	145	405	NLGA
	1.0 and higher	0.55	175	565	SPIB
Southern Pine	1.8*	0.57*	190*	805*	SPIB
	1.9 and higher	0.57	190	805	SPIB
	1.2 and higher	0.42	135	425	NLGA
Spruce-Pine-Fir	1.8 to 1.9	0.46	160	525	NLGA
	2.0 and higher	0.50	170	615	NLGA
	1.0 and higher	0.36	135	335	NELMA, NSLB, WCLIB, WWPA
	1.2 to 1.9	0.42	150	465	NELMA, NSLB
Sprce-Pine-Fir (S)	1.2 to 1.7	0.42	150	465	WWPA
	1.8 to 1.9	0.46	160	555	
	2.0 and higher	0.50	175	645	NELMA, NSLB, WWPA
Western Cedars	1.0 and higher	0.36	155	425	WCLIB, WWPA
Western Woods	1.0 and higher	0.36	135	335	WCLIB, WWPA

* 1.8E southern pine marked with a specific gravity of 0.55 on the grade stamp has a shear parallel to grain, F_v, of 175 psi and compression perpendicular to grain, $F_{c\perp}$, of 565 psi.

3. **MODULUS OF ELASTICITY, E, AND TENSION PARALLEL TO GRAIN, F_t.** For any given bending design value, F_b, the modulus of elasticity, E, and tension parallel to grain, F_t, design value may vary depending upon species, timber source, or other variables. The "E" and "F_t" values included in the "F_b-E" grade designations in Table 4C are those usually associated with each "F_b" level. Grade stamps may show higher or lower values if machine rating indicates the assignment is appropriate. Where the "E" or "F_t" values shown on a grade stamp differ from Table 4C values associated with the "F_b" on the grade stamp, the values on the stamp shall be used in design, and the "F_c" value associated with the "F_b" value in Table 4C shall be used.

4. **COMPRESSION PARALLEL TO GRAIN, F_c.** This grade requires "F_c" qualification and quality control.

Table 4D Adjustment Factors

Size Factor, C_F

When visually graded timbers are subjected to loads applied to the narrow face, tabulated design values shall be multiplied by the following size factors:

Size Factors, C_F

Depth	F_b	F_t	F_c
d > 12"	$(12/d)^{1/9}$	1.0	1.0
d ≤ 12"	1.0	1.0	1.0

Flat Use Factor, C_{fu}

When members designated as Beams and Stringers* in Table 4D are subjected to loads applied to the wide face, tabulated design values shall be multiplied by the following flat use factors:

Flat Use Factor, C_{fu}

Grade	F_b	E and E_{min}	Other Properties
Select Structural	0.86	1.00	1.00
No.1	0.74	0.90	1.00
No.2	1.00	1.00	1.00

*"Beams and Stringers" are defined in NDS 4.1.3 (also see Table 1B).

Wet Service Factor, C_M

When timbers are used where moisture content will exceed 19% for an extended time period, design values shall be multiplied by the appropriate wet service factor from the following table (for Southern Pine and Mixed Southern Pine, use tabulated design values without further adjustment):

Wet Service Factors, C_M

F_b	F_t	F_v	$F_{c\perp}$	F_c	E and E_{min}
1.00	1.00	1.00	0.67	0.91	1.00

Table 4D Reference Design Values for Visually Graded Timbers (5" x 5" and larger)[1,3]

(Tabulated design values are for normal load duration and dry service conditions, unless specified otherwise. See NDS 4.3 for a comprehensive description of design value adjustment factors.)

USE WITH TABLE 4D ADJUSTMENT FACTORS

Species and commercial Grade	Size classification	Bending F_b	Tension parallel to grain F_t	Shear parallel to grain F_v	Compression perpendicular to grain $F_{c\perp}$	Compression parallel to grain F_c	Modulus of Elasticity E	Modulus of Elasticity E_{min}	Specific Gravity[4] G	Grading Rules Agency
ALASKA CEDAR										
Select Structural	Beams and Stringers	1,400	675	155	525	925	1,200,000	440,000		
No.1	Beams and Stringers	1,150	475	155	525	775	1,200,000	440,000		
No.2		750	300	155	525	500	1,000,000	370,000	0.47	WCLIB
Select Structural	Posts and Timbers	1,300	700	155	525	975	1,200,000	440,000		
No.1	Posts and Timbers	1,050	575	155	525	850	1,200,000	440,000		
No.2		625	350	155	525	600	1,000,000	370,000		
BALDCYPRESS										
Select Structural	5"x5" and Larger	1,150	750	200	615	1,050	1,300,000	470,000		
No.1	5"x5" and Larger	1,000	675	200	615	925	1,300,000	470,000	0.43	SPIB
No.2		625	425	175	615	600	1,000,000	370,000		
BALSAM FIR										
Select Structural	Beams and Stringers	1,350	900	125	305	950	1,400,000	510,000		
No.1	Beams and Stringers	1,100	750	125	305	800	1,400,000	510,000		
No.2		725	350	125	305	500	1,100,000	400,000	0.36	NELMA NSLB
Select Structural	Posts and Timbers	1,250	825	125	305	1,000	1,400,000	510,000		
No.1	Posts and Timbers	1,000	675	125	305	875	1,400,000	510,000		
No.2		575	375	125	305	400	1,100,000	400,000		
BEECH-BIRCH-HICKORY										
Select Structural	Beams and Stringers	1,650	975	180	715	975	1,500,000	550,000		
No.1	Beams and Stringers	1,400	700	180	715	825	1,500,000	550,000		
No.2		900	450	180	715	525	1,200,000	440,000	0.71	NELMA NSLB
Select Structural	Posts and Timbers	1,550	1,050	180	715	1,050	1,500,000	550,000		
No.1	Posts and Timbers	1,250	850	180	715	900	1,500,000	550,000		
No.2		725	475	180	715	425	1,200,000	440,000		
COAST SITKA SPRUCE										
Select Structural	Beams and Stringers	1,150	675	115	455	775	1,500,000	550,000		
No.1	Beams and Stringers	950	475	115	455	650	1,500,000	550,000		
No.2		625	325	115	455	425	1,200,000	440,000	0.43	NLGA
Select Structural	Posts and Timbers	1,100	725	115	455	825	1,500,000	550,000		
No.1	Posts and Timbers	875	575	115	455	725	1,500,000	550,000		
No.2		525	350	115	455	500	1,200,000	440,000		
DOUGLAS FIR-LARCH										
Dense Select Structural	Beams and Stringers	1,900	1,100	170	730	1,300	1,700,000	620,000		
Select Structural	Beams and Stringers	1,600	950	170	625	1,100	1,600,000	580,000		
Dense No. 1	Beams and Stringers	1,550	775	170	730	1,100	1,700,000	620,000		
No. 1		1,350	675	170	625	925	1,600,000	580,000		
No. 2		875	425	170	625	600	1,300,000	470,000	0.50	WCLIB
Dense Select Structural	Posts and Timbers	1,750	1,150	170	730	1,350	1,700,000	620,000		
Select Structural	Posts and Timbers	1,500	1,000	170	625	1,150	1,600,000	580,000		
Dense No. 1	Posts and Timbers	1,400	950	170	730	1,200	1,700,000	620,000		
No. 1		1,200	825	170	625	1,000	1,600,000	580,000		
No. 2		750	475	170	625	700	1,300,000	470,000		
Dense Select Structural	Beams and Stringers	1,900	1,100	170	730	1,300	1,700,000	620,000		
Select Structural	Beams and Stringers	1,600	950	170	625	1,100	1,600,000	580,000		
Dense No. 1	Beams and Stringers	1,550	775	170	730	1,100	1,700,000	620,000		
No. 1	Beams and Stringers	1,350	675	170	625	925	1,600,000	580,000		
No. 2 Dense		1,000	500	170	730	700	1,400,000	510,000		
No. 2		875	425	170	625	600	1,300,000	470,000	0.50	WWPA
Dense Select Structural	Posts and Timbers	1,750	1,150	170	730	1,350	1,700,000	620,000		
Select Structural	Posts and Timbers	1,500	1,000	170	625	1,150	1,600,000	580,000		
Dense No. 1	Posts and Timbers	1,400	950	170	730	1,200	1,700,000	620,000		
No. 1	Posts and Timbers	1,200	825	170	625	1,000	1,600,000	580,000		
No. 2 Dense		850	550	170	730	825	1,400,000	510,000		
No. 2		750	475	170	625	700	1,300,000	470,000		

4

REFERENCE DESIGN VALUES

Table 4D (Cont.) Reference Design Values for Visually Graded Timbers (5" x 5" and larger)[1]

(Tabulated design values are for normal load duration and dry service conditions, unless specified otherwise. See NDS 4.3 for a comprehensive description of design value adjustment factors.)

USE WITH TABLE 4D ADJUSTMENT FACTORS

Species and commercial Grade	Size classification	Design values in pounds per square inch (psi)							Specific Gravity[4]	Grading Rules Agency
		Bending	Tension parallel to grain	Shear parallel to grain	Compression perpendicular to grain	Compression parallel to grain	Modulus of Elasticity			
		F_b	F_t	F_v	$F_{c\perp}$	F_c	E	E_{min}	G	
DOUGLAS FIR-LARCH (NORTH)										
Select Structural	Beams and Stringers	1,600	950	170	625	1,100	1,600,000	580,000		
No.1		1,300	675	170	625	925	1,600,000	580,000		
No.2		875	425	170	625	600	1,300,000	470,000	0.49	NLGA
Select Structural	Posts and Timbers	1,500	1,000	170	625	1,150	1,600,000	580,000		
No.1		1,200	825	170	625	1,000	1,600,000	580,000		
No.2		725	475	170	625	700	1,300,000	470,000		
DOUGLAS FIR-SOUTH										
Select Structural	Beams and Stringers	1,550	900	165	520	1,000	1,200,000	440,000		
No.1		1,300	625	165	520	850	1,200,000	440,000		
No.2		825	425	165	520	550	1,000,000	370,000	0.46	WWPA
Select Structural	Posts and Timbers	1,450	950	165	520	1,050	1,200,000	440,000		
No.1		1,150	775	165	520	925	1,200,000	440,000		
No.2		675	450	165	520	650	1,000,000	370,000		
EASTERN HEMLOCK										
Select Structural	Beams and Stringers	1,350	925	155	550	950	1,200,000	440,000		
No.1		1,150	775	155	550	800	1,200,000	440,000		
No.2		750	375	155	550	550	900,000	330,000	0.41	NELMA NSLB
Select Structural	Posts and Timbers	1,250	850	155	550	1,000	1,200,000	440,000		
No.1		1,050	700	155	500	875	1,200,000	440,000		
No.2		600	400	155	550	400	900,000	330,000		
EASTERN HEMLOCK-TAMARACK										
Select Structural	Beams and Stringers	1,400	925	155	555	950	1,200,000	440,000		
No.1		1,150	775	155	555	800	1,200,000	440,000		
No.2		750	375	155	555	500	900,000	330,000	0.41	NELMA NSLB
Select Structural	Posts and Timbers	1,300	875	155	555	1,000	1,200,000	440,000		
No.1		1,050	700	155	555	875	1,200,000	440,000		
No.2		600	400	155	555	400	900,000	330,000		
EASTERN HEMLOCK-TAMARACK (N)										
Select Structural	Beams and Stringers	1,450	850	165	555	950	1,300,000	470,000		
No.1		1,200	600	165	555	800	1,300,000	470,000		
No.2		775	400	165	555	500	1,100,000	400,000	0.47	NLGA
Select Structural	Posts and Timbers	1,350	900	165	555	1,000	1,300,000	470,000		
No.1		1,100	725	165	555	875	1,300,000	470,000		
No.2		650	425	165	555	600	1,100,000	400,000		
EASTERN SPRUCE										
Select Structural	Beams and Stringers	1,050	725	135	390	750	1,400,000	510,000		
No.1		900	600	135	390	625	1,400,000	510,000		
No.2		575	275	135	390	375	1,000,000	370,000	0.41	NELMA NSLB
Select Structural	Posts and Timbers	1,000	675	135	390	775	1,400,000	510,000		
No.1		800	550	135	390	675	1,400,000	510,000		
No.2		450	300	135	390	300	1,000,000	370,000		
EASTERN WHITE PINE										
Select Structural	Beams and Stringers	1,050	700	125	350	675	1,100,000	400,000		
No.1		875	600	125	350	575	1,100,000	400,000		
No.2		575	275	125	350	400	900,000	330,000	0.36	NELMA NSLB
Select Structural	Posts and Timbers	975	650	125	350	725	1,100,000	400,000		
No.1		800	525	125	350	625	1,100,000	400,000		
No.2		450	300	125	350	325	900,000	330,000		
HEM-FIR										
Select Structural	Beams and Stringers	1,300	750	140	405	925	1,300,000	470,000		
No.1		1,050	525	140	405	750	1,300,000	470,000		
No.2		675	350	140	405	500	1,100,000	400,000	0.43	WCLIB WWPA
Select Structural	Posts and Timbers	1,200	800	140	405	975	1,300,000	470,000		
No.1		975	650	140	405	850	1,300,000	470,000		
No.2		575	375	140	405	575	1,100,000	400,000		

Table 4D (Cont.) Reference Design Values for Visually Graded Timbers (5" x 5" and larger)[1,3]

(Tabulated design values are for normal load duration and dry service conditions, unless specified otherwise. See NDS 4.3 for a comprehensive description of design value adjustment factors.)

USE WITH TABLE 4D ADJUSTMENT FACTORS

| Species and commercial Grade | Size classification | Design values in pounds per square inch (psi) | | | | | | | Specific Gravity[4] | Grading Rules Agency |
		Bending F_b	Tension parallel to grain F_t	Shear parallel to grain F_v	Compression perpendicular to grain $F_{c\perp}$	Compression parallel to grain F_c	Modulus of Elasticity E	E_{min}	G	
HEM-FIR (NORTH)										
Select Structural	Beams and Stringers	1,250	725	135	405	900	1,300,000	470,000		
No.1		1,000	500	135	405	750	1,300,000	470,000		
No.2		675	325	135	405	475	1,100,000	400,000	0.46	NLGA
Select Structural	Posts and Timbers	1,150	775	135	405	950	1,300,000	470,000		
No.1		925	625	135	405	850	1,300,000	470,000		
No.2		550	375	135	405	575	1,100,000	400,000		
MIXED MAPLE										
Select Structural	Beams and Stringers	1,150	700	180	620	725	1,100,000	400,000		
No.1		975	500	180	620	600	1,100,000	400,000		
No.2		625	325	180	620	375	900,000	330,000	0.55	NELMA
Select Structural	Posts and Timbers	1,100	725	180	620	750	1,100,000	400,000		
No.1		875	600	180	620	650	1,100,000	400,000		
No.2		500	350	180	620	300	900,000	330,000		
MIXED OAK										
Select Structural	Beams and Stringers	1,350	800	155	800	825	1,000,000	370,000		
No.1		1,150	550	155	800	700	1,000,000	370,000		
No.2		725	375	155	800	450	800,000	290,000	0.68	NELMA
Select Structural	Posts and Timbers	1,250	850	155	800	875	1,000,000	370,000		
No.1		1,000	675	155	800	775	1,000,000	370,000		
No.2		575	400	155	800	350	800,000	290,000		
MIXED SOUTHERN PINE[2]		(Wet Service Conditons)								
Select Structural	5"x5" and Larger	1,500	1,000	165	375	900	1,300,000	470,000		
No.1		1,350	900	165	375	800	1,300,000	470,000	0.51	SPIB
No.2		850	550	165	375	525	1,000,000	370,000		
MOUNTAIN HEMLOCK										
Select Structural	Beams and Stringers	1,350	775	170	570	875	1,100,000	400,000		
No.1		1,100	550	170	570	725	1,100,000	400,000		
No.2		725	375	170	570	475	900,000	330,000	0.47	WCLIB WWPA
Select Structural	Posts and Timbers	1,250	825	170	570	925	1,100,000	400,000		
No.1		1,000	675	170	570	800	1,100,000	400,000		
No.2		625	400	170	570	550	900,000	330,000		
NORTHERN PINE										
Select Structural	Beams and Stringers	1,250	850	135	435	850	1,300,000	470,000		
No.1		1,050	700	135	435	725	1,300,000	470,000		
No.2		675	350	135	435	450	1,000,000	370,000	0.42	NELMA NSLB
Select Structural	Posts and Timbers	1,150	800	135	435	900	1,300,000	470,000		
No.1		950	650	135	435	800	1,300,000	470,000		
No.2		550	375	135	435	375	1,000,000	370,000		
NORTHERN RED OAK										
Select Structural	Beams and Stringers	1,600	950	205	885	950	1,300,000	470,000		
No.1		1,350	675	205	885	800	1,300,000	470,000		
No.2		875	425	205	885	500	1,000,000	370,000	0.68	NELMA
Select Structural	Posts and Timbers	1,500	1,000	205	885	1,000	1,300,000	470,000		
No.1		1,200	800	205	885	875	1,300,000	470,000		
No.2		700	475	205	885	400	1,000,000	370,000		
NORTHERN WHITE CEDAR										
Select Structural	Beams and Stringers	900	600	115	370	600	700,000	260,000		
No.1		750	500	115	370	500	700,000	260,000		
No.2		500	250	115	370	325	600,000	220,000	0.31	NELMA
Select Structural	Posts and Timbers	850	575	115	370	650	700,000	260,000		
No.1		675	450	115	370	550	700,000	260,000		
No.2		400	250	115	370	250	600,000	220,000		
PONDEROSA PINE										
Select Structural	Beams and Stringers	1,100	725	130	535	750	1,100,000	400,000		
No.1		925	500	130	535	625	1,100,000	400,000		
No.2		600	300	130	535	400	900,000	330,000	0.43	NLGA
Select Structural	Posts and Timbers	1,000	675	130	535	800	1,100,000	400,000		
No.1		825	550	130	535	700	1,100,000	400,000		
No.2		475	325	130	535	325	900,000	330,000		

4

REFERENCE DESIGN VALUES

Table 4D (Cont.) Reference Design Values for Visually Graded Timbers (5" x 5" and larger)[1]

(Tabulated design values are for normal load duration and dry service conditions, unless specified otherwise. See NDS 4.3 for a comprehensive description of design value adjustment factors.)

USE WITH TABLE 4D ADJUSTMENT FACTORS

Species and commercial Grade	Size classification	Design values in pounds per square inch (psi)							Specific Gravity[4] G	Grading Rules Agency
		Bending F_b	Tension parallel to grain F_t	Shear parallel to grain F_v	Compression perpendicular to grain $F_{c\perp}$	Compression parallel to grain F_c	Modulus of Elasticity			
							E	E_{min}		
RED MAPLE										
Select Structural	Beams and Stringers	1,500	875	195	615	900	1,500,000	550,000		
No.1		1,250	625	195	615	750	1,500,000	550,000		
No.2		800	400	195	615	475	1,200,000	440,000	0.58	NELMA
Select Structural	Posts and Timbers	1,400	925	195	615	950	1,500,000	550,000		
No.1		1,150	750	195	615	825	1,500,000	550,000		
No.2		650	425	195	615	375	1,200,000	440,000		
RED OAK										
Select Structural	Beams and Stringers	1,350	800	155	820	825	1,200,000	440,000		
No.1		1,150	550	155	820	700	1,200,000	440,000		
No.2		725	375	155	820	450	1,000,000	370,000	0.67	NELMA
Select Structural	Posts and Timbers	1,250	850	155	820	875	1,200,000	440,000		
No.1		1,000	675	155	820	775	1,200,000	440,000		
No.2		575	400	155	820	350	1,000,000	370,000		
RED PINE										
Select Structural	Beams and Stringers	1,050	625	130	440	725	1,100,000	400,000		
No.1		875	450	130	440	600	1,100,000	400,000		
No.2		575	300	130	440	375	900,000	330,000	0.44	NLGA
Select Structural	Posts and Timbers	1,000	675	130	440	775	1,100,000	400,000		
No.1		800	550	130	440	675	1,100,000	400,000		
No.2		475	325	130	440	475	900,000	330,000		
REDWOOD										
Clear Structural		1,850	1,250	145	650	1,650	1,300,000	470,000	0.44	
Select Structural		1,400	950	145	650	1,200	1,300,000	470,000	0.44	
Select Structural Open Grain		1,100	750	145	420	900	1,000,000	370,000	0.37	
No. 1	5"x5" and Larger	1,200	800	145	650	1,050	1,300,000	470,000	0.44	RIS
No. 1 Open Grain		950	650	145	420	800	1,000,000	370,000	0.37	
No. 2		1,000	525	145	650	900	1,100,000	400,000	0.44	
No. 2 Open Grain		750	400	145	420	650	900,000	330,000	0.37	
SITKA SPRUCE										
Select Structural	Beams and Stringers	1,200	675	140	435	825	1,300,000	470,000		
No.1		1,000	500	140	435	675	1,300,000	470,000		
No.2		650	325	140	435	450	1,000,000	370,000	0.43	WCLIB
Select Structural	Posts and Timbers	1,150	750	140	435	875	1,300,000	470,000		
No.1		925	600	140	435	750	1,300,000	470,000		
No.2		550	350	140	435	525	1,000,000	370,000		
Select Structural	Beams and Stringers	1,200	675	140	435	825	1,300,000	470,000		
No.1		1,000	500	140	435	675	1,300,000	470,000		
No.2		650	325	140	435	450	1,100,000	400,000	0.43	WWPA
Select Structural	Posts and Timbers	1,150	750	140	435	875	1,300,000	470,000		
No.1		925	600	140	435	750	1,300,000	470,000		
No.2		550	350	140	435	525	1,100,000	400,000		
SOUTHERN PINE		(Wet Service Conditons)								
Dense Select Structural		1,750	1,200	165	440	1,100	1,600,000	580,000		
Select Structural		1,500	1,000	165	375	950	1,500,000	550,000		
No. 1 Dense		1,550	1,050	165	440	975	1,600,000	580,000		
No. 1		1,350	900	165	375	825	1,500,000	550,000		
No. 2 Dense	5" x 5" and Larger	975	650	165	440	625	1,300,000	470,000		
No. 2		850	550	165	375	525	1,200,000	440,000	0.55	SPIB
Dense Select Structural 86		2,100	1,400	165	440	1,300	1,600,000	580,000		
Dense Select Structural 72		1,750	1,200	165	440	1,100	1,600,000	580,000		
Dense Select Structural 65		1,600	1,050	165	440	1,000	1,600,000	580,000		

Table 4D (Cont.) Reference Design Values for Visually Graded Timbers (5" x 5" and larger)[1,3]

(Tabulated design values are for normal load duration and dry service conditions, unless specified otherwise. See NDS 4.3 for a comprehensive description of design value adjustment factors.)

USE WITH TABLE 4D ADJUSTMENT FACTORS

Species and commercial Grade	Size classification	Bending F_b	Tension parallel to grain F_t	Shear parallel to grain F_v	Compression perpendicular to grain $F_{c\perp}$	Compression parallel to grain F_c	Modulus of Elasticity E	E_{min}	Specific Gravity[4] G	Grading Rules Agency
SPRUCE-PINE-FIR										
Select Structural	Beams and Stringers	1,100	650	125	425	775	1,300,000	470,000		
No.1		900	450	125	425	625	1,300,000	470,000		
No.2		600	300	125	425	425	1,000,000	370,000	0.42	NLGA
Select Structural	Posts and Timbers	1,050	700	125	425	800	1,300,000	470,000		
No.1		850	550	125	425	700	1,300,000	470,000		
No.2		500	325	125	425	500	1,000,000	370,000		
SPRUCE-PINE-FIR (SOUTH)										
Select Structural	Beams and Stringers	1,050	625	125	335	675	1,200,000	440,000		
No.1		900	450	125	335	550	1,200,000	440,000		NELMA
No.2		575	300	125	335	375	1,000,000	370,000		NSLB
Select Structural	Posts and Timbers	1,000	675	125	335	700	1,200,000	440,000	0.36	WWPA
No.1		800	550	125	335	625	1,200,000	440,000		WCLIB
No.2		475	325	125	335	425	1,000,000	370,000		
WESTERN CEDARS										
Select Structural	Beams and Stringers	1,150	675	140	425	875	1,000,000	370,000		
No.1		975	475	140	425	725	1,000,000	370,000		
No.2		625	325	140	425	475	800,000	290,000	0.36	WCLIB
Select Structural	Posts and Timbers	1,100	725	140	425	925	1,000,000	370,000		WWPA
No.1		875	600	140	425	800	1,000,000	370,000		
No.2		550	350	140	425	550	800,000	290,000		
WESTERN CEDARS (NORTH)										
Select Structural	Beams and Stringers	1,150	675	130	425	850	1,000,000	370,000		
No.1		925	475	130	425	700	1,000,000	370,000		
No.2		625	300	130	425	450	800,000	290,000	0.35	NLGA
Select Structural	Posts and Timbers	1,050	700	130	425	900	1,000,000	370,000		
No.1		875	575	130	425	800	1,000,000	370,000		
No.2		500	350	130	425	550	800,000	290,000		
WESTERN HEMLOCK										
Select Structural	Beams and Stringers	1,400	825	170	410	1,000	1,400,000	510,000		
No.1		1,150	575	170	410	850	1,400,000	510,000		
No.2		750	375	170	410	550	1,100,000	400,000	0.47	WCLIB
Select Structural	Posts and Timbers	1,300	875	170	410	1,100	1,400,000	510,000		WWPA
No.1		1,050	700	170	410	950	1,400,000	510,000		
No.2		650	425	170	410	650	1,100,000	400,000		
WESTERN HEMLOCK (NORTH)										
Select Structural	Beams and Stringers	1,400	825	135	410	1,000	1,400,000	510,000		
No.1		1,150	575	135	410	850	1,400,000	510,000		
No.2		750	375	135	410	550	1,100,000	400,000		
Select Structural	Posts and Timbers	1,300	875	135	410	1,100	1,400,000	510,000	0.46	NLGA
No.1		1,050	700	135	410	950	1,400,000	510,000		
No.2		650	425	135	410	650	1,100,000	400,000		
WESTERN WHITE PINE										
Select Structural	Beams and Stringers	1,050	600	120	375	775	1,300,000	470,000		
No.1		850	425	120	375	625	1,300,000	470,000		
No.2		550	275	120	375	400	1,000,000	370,000		
Select Structural	Posts and Timbers	975	650	120	375	800	1,300,000	470,000	0.40	NLGA
No.1		775	525	120	375	700	1,300,000	470,000		
No.2		450	300	120	375	500	1,000,000	370,000		

4

REFERENCE DESIGN VALUES

Table 4D (Cont.) Reference Design Values for Visually Graded Timbers (5" x 5" and larger)[1]

(Tabulated design values are for normal load duration and dry service conditions, unless specified otherwise. See NDS 4.3 for a comprehensive description of design value adjustment factors.)

USE WITH TABLE 4D ADJUSTMENT FACTORS

| Species and commercial Grade | Size classification | Design values in pounds per square inch (psi) | | | | | | | Specific Gravity[4] | Grading Rules Agency |
		Bending F_b	Tension parallel to grain F_t	Shear parallel to grain F_v	Compression perpendicular to grain $F_{c\perp}$	Compression parallel to grain F_c	Modulus of Elasticity E	E_{min}	G	
WESTERN WOODS										
Select Structural	Beams and Stringers	1,050	625	125	345	750	1,100,000	400,000		
No.1	Beams and Stringers	900	450	125	345	625	1,100,000	400,000		
No.2	Beams and Stringers	575	300	125	345	425	900,000	330,000	0.36	WCLIB WWPA
Select Structural	Posts and Timbers	1,000	675	125	345	800	1,100,000	400,000		
No.1	Posts and Timbers	800	525	125	345	700	1,100,000	400,000		
No.2	Posts and Timbers	475	325	125	345	475	900,000	330,000		
WHITE OAK										
Select Structural	Beams and Stringers	1,400	825	205	800	900	1,000,000	370,000		
No.1	Beams and Stringers	1,200	575	205	800	775	1,000,000	370,000		
No.2	Beams and Stringers	750	375	205	800	475	800,000	290,000	0.73	NELMA
Select Structural	Posts and Timbers	1,300	875	205	800	950	1,000,000	370,000		
No.1	Posts and Timbers	1,050	700	205	800	825	1,000,000	370,000		
No.2	Posts and Timbers	600	400	205	800	400	800,000	290,000		

Footnotes to Table 4D

1. **LUMBER DIMENSIONS.** Tabulated design values are applicable to lumber that will be used under dry conditions such as in most covered structures. For 5 and thicker lumber, the GREEN dressed sizes shall be permitted to be used (see Table 1A) because design values have been adjusted to compensate for any los in size by shrinkage which may occur.

2. **SPRUCE PINE.** To obtain recommended design values for Spruce Pine graded to Southern Pine Inspection Bureau (SPIB) rules, multiply the appropriate desig values for Mixed Southern Pine by the corresponding conversion factor shown below and round to the nearest 100,000 psi for E; to the nearest 10,000 psi for E to the next lower multiple of 5 psi for F_v and $F_{c\perp}$; to the next lower multiple of 50 psi for F_b, F_t, and F_c if 1,000 psi or greater, 25 psi otherwise.

CONVERSION FACTORS FOR DETERMINING DESIGN VALUES FOR SPRUCE PINE

	Bending F_b	Tension parallel to grain F_t	Shear parallel to grain F_v	Compression perpendicular to grain $F_{c\perp}$	Compression parallel to grain F_c	Modulus of Elasticity E and E_{min}
Conversion Factor	0.78	0.78	0.98	0.73	0.78	0.82

3. When individual species or species groups are combined, the design values to be used for the combination shall be the lowest design values for each individual species or species group for each design property.

4. Specific gravity, G, based on weight and volume when oven-dry.

Table 4E Adjustment Factors

Wet Service Factor, C_M

When decking is used where moisture content will exceed 19% for an extended time period, design values shall be multiplied by the appropriate wet service factors from the following table (for surfaced dry Southern Pine decking use tabulated surfaced green design values for wet service conditions without further adjustment):

Wet Service Factors, C_M

F_b	$F_{c\perp}$	E and E_{min}
0.85*	0.67	0.9

* when $(F_b)(C_F) \leq 1{,}150$ psi, $C_M = 1.0$

Flat Use Factor, C_{fu}

Tabulated bending design values, F_b, for decking have already been adjusted for flatwise usage (load applied to wide face).

Size Factor, C_F

Bending design values for all species of decking except Redwood are based on 4" thick decking. When 2" thick or 3" thick decking is used, the bending design values, F_b, for all species except Redwood shall be multiplied by the following size factors:

Size Factors, C_F

Thickness	C_F
2"	1.10
3"	1.04

Repetitive Member Factor, C_r

Tabulated bending design values for repetitive member uses, $(F_b)(C_r)$, for decking have already been multiplied by the repetitive member factor, C_r.

4

REFERENCE DESIGN VALUES

Table 4E   Reference Design Values for Visually Graded Decking[1,2]

(Tabulated design values are for normal load duration and dry service conditions, unless specified otherwise. See NDS 4.3 for a comprehensive description of design value adjustment factors.)

USE WITH TABLE 4E ADJUSTMENT FACTORS

Species and commercial grade	Size classification	Bending Single Member F_b	Bending Repetitive Member $(F_b)(C_r)$	Compression perpendicular to grain $F_{c\perp}$	Modulus of Elasticity E	Modulus of Elasticity E_{min}	Specific Gravity[3] G	Grading Rules Agency
BALSAM FIR								
Select	2"-4" thick	—	1,650	—	1,500,000	550,000	0.36	NELMA
Commercial	4"-12"wide	—	1,400	—	1,300,000	470,000		
COAST SITKA SPRUCE								
Select	2"-4" thick	1,250	1,450	455	1,700,000	620,000	0.43	NLGA
Commercial	4"& wider	1,050	1,200	455	1,500,000	550,000		
COAST SPECIES								
Select	2"-4" thick	1,250	1,450	370	1,500,000	550,000	0.43	NLGA
Commercial	4"& wider	1,050	1,200	370	1,400,000	510,000		
DOUGLAS FIR-LARCH								
Select Dex	2"-4" thick	1,750	2,000	625	1,800,000	660,000	0.50	WCLIB
Commercial Dex	6"-8"wide	1,450	1,650	625	1,700,000	620,000		
Selected	2"-4" thick	1,750	2,000	625	1,800,000	660,000	0.50	WWPA
Commercial	4"-12"wide	1,450	1,650	625	1,700,000	620,000		
DOUGLAS FIR-LARCH (NORTH)								
Select	2"-4" thick	1,750	2,000	625	1,800,000	660,000	0.49	NLGA
Commercial	4"& wider	1,450	1,650	625	1,700,000	620,000		
DOUGLAS FIR-SOUTH								
Selected	2"-4" thick	1,650	1,900	520	1,400,000	510,000	0.46	WWPA
Commercial	4"-12"wide	1,400	1,600	520	1,300,000	470,000		
EASTERN HEMLOCK-TAMARACK								
Select	2"-4" thick	—	1,700	—	1,300,000	470,000	0.41	NELMA
Commercial	4"-12"wide	—	1,450	—	1,100,000	400,000		
EASTERN HEMLOCK-TAMARACK (NORTH)								
Select	2"-4" thick	1,500	1,700	555	1,300,000	470,000	0.47	NLGA
Commercial	4"& wider	1,250	1,450	555	1,100,000	400,000		
EASTERN SPRUCE								
Select	2"-4" thick	—	1,300	—	1,500,000	550,000	0.41	NELMA
Commercial	4"-12"wide	—	1,100	—	1,400,000	510,000		
EASTERN WHITE PINE								
Select	2"-4" thick	—	1,300	—	1,200,000	440,000	0.36	NELMA
Commercial	4"-12"wide	—	1,100	—	1,100,000	400,000		
EASTERN WHITE PINE (NORTH)								
Select	2"-4" thick	900	1,050	350	1,200,000	440,000	0.38	NLGA
Commercial	4"& wider	775	875	350	1,100,000	400,000		
HEM-FIR								
Select Dex	2"-4" thick	1,400	1,600	405	1,500,000	550,000	0.43	WCLIB
Commercial Dex	6"-8"wide	1,150	1,350	405	1,400,000	510,000		
Selected	2"-4" thick	1,400	1,600	405	1,500,000	550,000	0.43	WWPA
Commercial	4"-12"wide	1,150	1,350	405	1,400,000	510,000		
HEM-FIR (NORTH)								
Select	2"-4" thick	1,350	1,500	405	1,500,000	550,000	0.46	NLGA
Commercial	4"& wider	1,100	1,300	405	1,400,000	510,000		
NORTHERN PINE								
Select	2"-4" thick	—	1,550	—	1,400,000	510,000	0.42	NELMA
Commercial	4"-12"wide	—	1,300	—	1,300,000	470,000		
NORTHERN SPECIES								
Select	2"-4" thick	900	1,050	350	1,100,000	400,000	0.35	NLGA
Commercial	4"& wider	775	875	350	1,000,000	370,000		

Table 4E (Cont.)   Reference Design Values for Visually Graded Decking[1,2]

(Tabulated design values are for normal load duration and dry service conditions, unless specified otherwise. See NDS 4.3 for a comprehensive description of design value adjustment factors.)

USE WITH TABLE 4E ADJUSTMENT FACTORS

Species and commercial grade	Size classification	Bending — Single Member F_b	Bending — Repetitive Member $(F_b)(C_r)$	Compression perpendicular to grain $F_{c\perp}$	Modulus of Elasticity E	Modulus of Elasticity E_{min}	Specific Gravity[3] G	Grading Rules Agency
NORTHERN WHITE CEDAR								
Select	2"-4" thick	—	1,100	—	800,000	290,000	0.31	NELMA
Commercial	4"-12"wide	—	950	—	700,000	260,000		
PONDEROSA PINE								
Select	2"-4" thick	1,200	1,400	535	1,300,000	470,000	0.43	NLGA
Commercial	4"& wider	1,000	1,150	535	1,100,000	400,000		
RED PINE								
Select	2"-4" thick	1,150	1,350	440	1,300,000	470,000	0.44	NLGA
Commercial	4"& wider	975	1,100	440	1,200,000	440,000		
REDWOOD								
Select, Close grain	2" thick	1,850	2,150	—	1,400,000	510,000	0.44	
Select		1,450	1,700	—	1,100,000	400,000	0.37	
Commercial	6"& wider	1,200	1,350	—	1,000,000	370,000	0.37	RIS
Deck Heart and	2" thick 4" wide	400	450	420	900,000	330,000	0.37	
Deck Common	2" thick 6" wide	700	800	420	900,000	330,000	0.37	
SITKA SPRUCE								
Select Dex	2"-4" thick	1,300	1,500	435	1,500,000	550,000	0.43	WCLIB
Commercial Dex	6"-8"wide	1,100	1,250	435	1,300,000	470,000		
SOUTHERN PINE		(Surfaced dry – Used in dry service conditions — 19% or less moisture content)						
Dense Standard		2,000	2,300	660	1,800,000	660,000		
Dense Select	2"-4" thick	1,650	1,900	660	1,600,000	580,000		
Select		1,400	1,650	565	1,600,000	580,000	0.55	SPIB
Dense Commercial	2" & wider	1,650	1,900	660	1,600,000	580,000		
Commercial		1,400	1,650	565	1,600,000	580,000		
SOUTHERN PINE		(Surfaced Green – Used in any service condition)						
Dense Standard		1,600	1,800	440	1,600,000	580,000		
Dense Select	2-1/2"-4" thick	1,350	1,500	440	1,400,000	510,000		
Select		1,150	1,300	375	1,400,000	510,000	0.55	SPIB
Dense Commercial	2" & wider	1,350	1,500	440	1,400,000	510,000		
Commercial		1,150	1,300	375	1,400,000	510,000		
SPRUCE-PINE-FIR								
Select	2"-4" thick	1,200	1,400	425	1,500,000	550,000	0.42	NLGA
Commercial	4"& wider	1,000	1,150	425	1,300,000	470,000		
SPRUCE-PINE-FIR (SOUTH)								
Selected	2"-4" thick	1,150	1,350	335	1,400,000	510,000	0.36	NELMA WWPA
Commercial	4"-12"wide	950	1,100	335	1,200,000	440,000		
WESTERN CEDARS								
Select Dex	2"-4" thick	1,250	1,450	425	1,100,000	400,000	0.36	WCLIB
Commercial Dex	6"-8"wide	1,050	1,200	425	1,000,000	370,000		
Selected	2"-4" thick	1,250	1,450	425	1,100,000	400,000	0.36	WWPA
Commercial	4"-12"wide	1,050	1,200	425	1,000,000	370,000		
WESTERN CEDARS (NORTH)								
Select	2"-4" thick	1,200	1,400	425	1,100,000	400,000	0.35	NLGA
Commercial	4"& wider	1,050	1,200	425	1,000,000	370,000		

4

REFERENCE DESIGN VALUES

Reference Design Values for Visually Graded Decking[1,2]

(Tabulated design values are for normal load duration and dry service conditions, unless specified otherwise. See NDS 4.3 for a comprehensive description of design value adjustment factors.)

USE WITH TABLE 4E ADJUSTMENT FACTORS

Species and commercial grade	Size classification	Bending Single Member F_b	Bending Repetitive Member $(F_b)(C_r)$	Compression perpendicular to grain $F_{c\perp}$	Modulus of Elasticity E	Modulus of Elasticity E_{min}	Specific Gravity[3] G	Grading Rules Agency
WESTERN HEMLOCK								
Select Dex	2"-4" thick	1,500	1,750	410	1,600,000	580,000	0.47	WCLIB
Commercial Dex	6" & wider	1,300	1,450	410	1,400,000	510,000		
WESTERN HEMLOCK (NORTH)								
Select	2"-4" thick	1,500	1,750	410	1,600,000	580,000	0.46	NLGA
Commercial	4" & wider	1,300	1,450	410	1,400,000	510,000		
WESTERN WHITE PINE								
Select	2"-4" thick	1,100	1,300	375	1,400,000	510,000	0.40	NLGA
Commercial	4" & wider	925	1,050	375	1,300,000	470,000		
WESTERN WOODS								
Selected	2"-4" thick	1,150	1,300	335	1,200,000	440,000	0.36	WWPA
Commercial	4"-12" wide	950	1,100	335	1,100,000	400,000		

1. **LUMBER DIMENSIONS.** Tabulated design values are applicable to lumber that will be used under dry conditions such as in most covered structures. For 2" to 4" thick lumber the DRY dressed sizes shall be used (see Table 1A) regardless of the moisture content at the time of manufacture or use. In calculating design values, the natural gain in strength and stiffness that occurs as lumber dries has been taken into consideration as well as the reduction in size that occurs when unseasoned lumber shrinks. The gain in load carrying capacity due to increased strength and stiffness resulting from drying more than offsets the design effect of size reductions due to shrinkage.
2. When individual species or species groups are combined, the design values to be used for the combination shall be the lowest design values for each individual species or species group for each design property.
3. Specific gravity, G, based on weight and volume when oven-dry.

Table 4F Adjustment Factors

Repetitive Member Factor, C_r

Bending design values, F_b, for dimension lumber 2" to 4" thick shall be multiplied by the repetitive member factor, $C_r = 1.15$, when such members are used as joists, truss chords, rafters, studs, planks, decking, or similar members which are in contact or spaced not more than 24" on center, are not less than 3 in number, and are joined by floor, roof, or other load distributing elements adequate to support the design load.

Wet Service Factor, C_M

When dimension lumber is used where moisture content will exceed 19% for an extended time period, design values shall be multiplied by the appropriate wet service factors from the following table:

Wet Service Factors, C_M

F_b	F_t	F_v	$F_{c\perp}$	F_c	E and E_{min}
0.85*	1.0	0.97	0.67	0.8**	0.9

* when $(F_b)(C_F) \leq 1{,}150$ psi, $C_M = 1.0$
** when $(F_c)(C_F) \leq 750$ psi, $C_M = 1.0$

Flat Use Factor, C_{fu}

Bending design values adjusted by size factors are based on edgewise use (load applied to narrow face). When dimension lumber is used flatwise (load applied to wide face), the bending design value, F_b, shall also be multiplied by the following flat use factors:

Flat Use Factors, C_{fu}

Width	Thickness (breadth)	
(depth)	2" & 3"	4"
2" & 3"	1.0	—
4"	1.1	1.0
5"	1.1	1.05
6"	1.15	1.05
8"	1.15	1.05
10" & wider	1.2	1.1

NOTE

To facilitate the use of Table 4F, shading has been employed to distinguish design values based on a 4" nominal width (Construction, Standard, and Utility grades) or a 6" nominal width (Stud grade) from design values based on a 12" nominal width (Select Structural, No.1 & Btr, No.1, No.2, and No.3 grades).

Size Factor, C_F

Tabulated bending, tension, and compression parallel to grain design values for dimension lumber 2" to 4" thick shall be multiplied by the following size factors:

Size Factors, C_F

Grades	Width (depth)	F_b Thickness (breadth) 2" & 3"	F_b Thickness (breadth) 4"	F_t	F_c
Select Structural, No.1 & Btr, No.1, No.2, No.3	2", 3", & 4"	1.5	1.5	1.5	1.15
	5"	1.4	1.4	1.4	1.1
	6"	1.3	1.3	1.3	1.1
	8"	1.2	1.3	1.2	1.05
	10"	1.1	1.2	1.1	1.0
	12"	1.0	1.1	1.0	1.0
	14" & wider	0.9	1.0	0.9	0.9
Stud	2", 3", & 4"	1.1	1.1	1.1	1.05
	5" & 6"	1.0	1.0	1.0	1.0
	8" & wider	Use No.3 Grade tabulated design values and size factors			
Construction, Standard	2", 3", & 4"	1.0	1.0	1.0	1.0
Utility	4"	1.0	1.0	1.0	1.0
	2" & 3"	0.4	—	0.4	0.6

4

REFERENCE DESIGN VALUES

Table 4F   Reference Design Values for Non-North American Visually Graded Dimension Lumber (2" - 4" thick)[1,3]

(Tabulated design values are for normal load duration and dry service conditions. See NDS 4.3 for a comprehensive description of design value adjustment factors.)

USE WITH TABLE 4F ADJUSTMENT FACTORS

Species and commercial Grade	Size classification	Design values in pounds per square inch (psi)							Specific Gravity[5]	Grading Rules Agency
		Bending F_b	Tension parallel to grain F_t	Shear parallel to grain F_v	Compression perpendicular to grain $F_{c\perp}$	Compression parallel to grain F_c	Modulus of Elasticity E	Modulus of Elasticity E_{min}	G	
AUSTRIAN SPRUCE - Austria & The Czech Republic										
Select Structural		1,500	675	175	260	1,250	1,700,000	620,000		
No. 1	2" & wider	1,000	450	175	260	1,100	1,600,000	580,000		
No. 2		925	400	175	260	1,050	1,500,000	550,000		
No. 3		525	225	175	260	625	1,300,000	470,000		
Stud	2" & wider	725	325	175	260	675	1,300,000	470,000	0.43	WCLIB
Construction		1,050	475	175	260	1,300	1,400,000	510,000		
Standard	2" - 4" wide	575	250	175	260	1,100	1,300,000	470,000		
Utility		275	125	175	260	725	1,200,000	440,000		
DOUGLAS FIR - France & Germany										
Select Structural		1,500	675	205	540	1,250	1,900,000	690,000		
No. 1	2" & wider	975	450	205	540	1,100	1,700,000	620,000		
No. 2		825	375	205	540	1,000	1,500,000	550,000		
No. 3		475	225	205	540	600	1,300,000	470,000		
Stud	2" & wider	650	300	205	540	650	1,300,000	470,000	0.48	WCLIB
Construction		925	425	205	540	1,250	1,400,000	510,000		
Standard	2" - 4" wide	525	225	205	540	1,050	1,300,000	470,000		
Utility		250	100	205	540	675	1,200,000	440,000		
DOUGLAS FIR/EUROPEAN LARCH - Austria, The Czech Republic, & Bavaria[2]										
Select Structural		1,900	850	195	440	1,400	1,800,000	660,000		
No. 1	2" & wider	1,400	625	195	440	1,250	1,700,000	620,000		
No. 2		1,350	600	195	440	1,250	1,600,000	580,000		
No. 3		775	350	195	440	700	1,400,000	510,000		
Stud	2" & wider	800	350	195	440	700	1,400,000	510,000	0.48	WCLIB
Construction		1,000	450	195	440	1,250	1,500,000	550,000		
Standard	2" - 4" wide	575	250	195	440	1,100	1,300,000	470,000		
Utility		275	125	195	440	700	1,300,000	470,000		
MONTANE PINE - South Africa										
Select Structural		975	425	135	325	1,100	1,300,000	470,000		
No. 1	2" & wider	650	300	135	325	950	1,100,000	400,000		
No. 2		600	275	135	325	850	1,000,000	370,000		
No. 3		350	150	135	325	475	900,000	330,000		
Stud	2" & wider	475	200	135	325	525	900,000	330,000	0.45	WCLIB
Construction		675	300	135	325	1,050	900,000	330,000		
Standard	2" - 4" wide	375	175	135	325	875	800,000	290,000		
Utility		175	75	135	325	575	800,000	290,000		
NORWAY SPRUCE - Estonia, Latvia, & Lithuania										
Select Structural		1,200	550	150	430	1,200	1,600,000	580,000		
No. 1	2" & wider	850	375	150	430	1,050	1,400,000	510,000		
No. 2		800	350	150	430	1,000	1,300,000	470,000		
No. 3		450	200	150	430	575	1,100,000	400,000		
Stud	2" & wider	625	275	150	430	625	1,100,000	400,000	0.42	WCLIB
Construction		900	400	150	430	1,200	1,200,000	440,000		
Standard	2" - 4" wide	500	225	150	430	1,050	1,100,000	400,000		
Utility		250	100	150	430	675	1,000,000	370,000		
NORWAY SPRUCE - Finland										
Select Structural		1,350	600	125	220	1,200	1,500,000	550,000		
No. 1	2" & wider	825	375	125	220	1,000	1,400,000	510,000		
No. 2		625	275	125	220	875	1,200,000	440,000		
No. 3		375	175	125	220	500	1,100,000	400,000		
Stud	2" & wider	575	250	125	220	600	1,100,000	400,000	0.42	WCLIB
Construction		725	325	125	220	1,100	1,100,000	400,000		
Standard	2" - 4" wide	400	175	125	220	900	1,000,000	370,000		
Utility		200	75	125	220	600	1,000,000	370,000		

Reference Design Values for Non-North American Visually Graded Dimension Lumber (2" - 4" thick)[1,3]

(Tabulated design values are for normal load duration and dry service conditions. See NDS 4.3 for a comprehensive description of design value adjustment factors.)

USE WITH TABLE 4F ADJUSTMENT FACTORS

Species and commercial Grade	Size classification	Design values in pounds per square inch (psi)							Specific Gravity[5]	Grading Rules Agency
		Bending	Tension parallel to grain	Shear parallel to grain	Compression perpendicular to grain	Compression parallel to grain	Modulus of Elasticity			
		F_b	F_t	F_v	$F_{c\perp}$	F_c	E	E_{min}	G	
NORWAY SPRUCE - Germany, NE France, & Switzerland										
Select Structural	2" & wider	1,200	550	170	355	1,200	1,600,000	580,000	0.42	WCLIB
No. 1		825	375	170	355	1,050	1,400,000	510,000		
No. 2		725	325	170	355	950	1,200,000	440,000		
No. 3		425	200	170	355	550	1,100,000	400,000		
Stud	2" & wider	575	250	170	355	600	1,100,000	400,000		
Construction		825	375	170	355	1,200	1,100,000	400,000		
Standard	2" - 4" wide	475	200	170	355	975	1,000,000	370,000		
Utility		225	100	170	355	650	900,000	330,000		
NORWAY SPRUCE - Romania & the Ukraine										
Select Structural	2" & wider	1,250	575	100	275	1,200	1,500,000	550,000	0.38	WCLIB
No. 1		850	375	100	275	1,050	1,400,000	510,000		
No. 2		725	325	100	275	950	1,200,000	440,000		
No. 3		425	200	100	275	550	1,100,000	400,000		
Stud	2" & wider	575	250	100	275	600	1,100,000	400,000		
Construction		850	375	100	275	1,200	1,100,000	400,000		
Standard	2" - 4" wide	475	200	100	275	1,000	1,000,000	370,000		
Utility		225	100	100	275	650	1,000,000	370,000		
NORWAY SPRUCE - Sweden										
Select Structural	2" & wider	1,250	550	170	285	1,200	1,600,000	580,000	0.42	WCLIB
No. 1		825	375	170	285	1,050	1,400,000	510,000		
No. 2		675	300	170	285	925	1,200,000	440,000		
No. 3		400	175	170	285	525	1,100,000	400,000		
Stud	2" & wider	550	250	170	285	575	1,100,000	400,000		
Construction		775	350	170	285	1,150	1,200,000	440,000		
Standard	2" - 4" wide	425	200	170	285	950	1,100,000	400,000		
Utility		200	100	170	285	625	1,000,000	370,000		
SCOTS PINE - Austria & The Czech Republic, Romania, & the Ukraine										
Select Structural	2" & wider	1,300	600	135	270	1,200	1,700,000	620,000	0.50	WCLIB
No. 1		900	400	135	270	1,050	1,600,000	580,000		
No. 2		775	350	135	270	1,000	1,400,000	510,000		
No. 3		450	200	135	270	575	1,300,000	470,000		
Stud	2" & wider	600	275	135	270	625	1,300,000	470,000		
Construction		875	400	135	270	1,200	1,300,000	470,000		
Standard	2" - 4" wide	500	225	135	270	1,000	1,200,000	440,000		
Utility		225	100	135	270	675	1,100,000	400,000		
SCOTS PINE - Estonia, Latvia, & Lithuania										
Select Structural	2" & wider	1,150	525	130	430	1,150	1,500,000	550,000	0.45	WCLIB
No. 1		800	350	130	430	1,050	1,400,000	510,000		
No. 2		750	325	130	430	975	1,200,000	440,000		
No. 3		425	200	130	430	550	1,100,000	400,000		
Stud	2" & wider	575	275	130	430	625	1,100,000	400,000		
Construction		850	375	130	430	1,200	1,100,000	400,000		
Standard	2" - 4" wide	475	225	130	430	1,000	1,000,000	370,000		
Utility		225	100	130	430	650	1,000,000	370,000		
SCOTS PINE - Finland										
Select Structural	2" & wider	1,300	600	150	210	1,200	1,500,000	550,000	0.48	WCLIB
No. 1		950	425	150	210	1,100	1,400,000	510,000		
No. 2		925	425	150	210	1,100	1,300,000	470,000		
No. 3		525	250	150	210	625	1,200,000	440,000		
Stud	2" & wider	725	325	150	210	675	1,200,000	440,000		
Construction		1,050	475	150	210	1,300	1,200,000	440,000		
Standard	2" - 4" wide	600	275	150	210	1,100	1,100,000	400,000		
Utility		275	125	150	210	725	1,000,000	370,000		

4

REFERENCE DESIGN VALUES

(Tabulated design values are for normal load duration and dry service conditions. See NDS 4.3 for a comprehensive description of design value adjustment factors.)

USE WITH TABLE 4F ADJUSTMENT FACTORS

Species and commercial Grade	Size classification	Design values in pounds per square inch (psi)							Specific Gravity[5]	Grading Rules Agency
		Bending	Tension parallel to grain	Shear parallel to grain	Compression perpendicular to grain	Compression parallel to grain	Modulus of Elasticity			
		F_b	F_t	F_v	$F_{c\perp}$	F_c	E	E_{min}	G	
SCOTS PINE - Germany[4]										
Select Structural	2" & wider	1,200	550	160	395	1,200	1,600,000	580,000	0.53	WCLIB
No. 1		800	375	160	395	1,050	1,400,000	510,000		
No. 2		700	325	160	395	950	1,100,000	400,000		
No. 3		400	175	160	395	550	1,000,000	370,000		
Stud	2" & wider	550	250	160	395	600	1,000,000	370,000		
Construction		800	375	160	395	1,150	1,100,000	400,000		
Standard	2" - 4" wide	450	200	160	395	975	1,000,000	370,000		
Utility		225	100	160	395	625	900,000	330,000		
SCOTS PINE - Sweden										
Select Structural	2" & wider	1,350	600	120	410	1,200	1,700,000	620,000	0.47	WCLIB
No. 1		825	375	120	410	1,000	1,500,000	550,000		
No. 2		575	250	120	410	825	1,200,000	440,000		
No. 3		325	150	120	410	475	1,100,000	400,000		
Stud	2" & wider	450	200	120	410	525	1,100,000	400,000		
Construction		650	300	120	410	1,050	1,200,000	440,000		
Standard	2" - 4" wide	375	175	120	410	850	1,100,000	400,000		
Utility		175	75	120	410	550	1,000,000	370,000		
SILVER FIR (Abies alba) - Germany, NE France, & Switzerland										
Select Structural	2" & wider	950	425	125	400	1,100	1,500,000	550,000	0.43	WCLIB
No. 1		725	325	125	400	975	1,400,000	510,000		
No. 2		725	325	125	400	950	1,300,000	470,000		
No. 3		425	200	125	400	550	1,100,000	400,000		
Stud	2" & wider	575	250	125	400	600	1,100,000	400,000		
Construction		825	375	125	400	1,150	1,200,000	440,000		
Standard	2" - 4" wide	475	200	125	400	975	1,100,000	400,000		
Utility		225	100	125	400	650	1,000,000	370,000		
SOUTHERN PINE - Misiones Argentina										
Select Structural	2" & wider	1,100	500	150	440	1,150	1,200,000	440,000	0.45	SPIB
No. 1		775	350	150	440	1,000	1,100,000	400,000		
No. 2		725	325	150	440	950	1,100,000	400,000		
No. 3		425	200	150	440	550	900,000	330,000		
Stud	2" & wider	575	250	150	440	600	900,000	330,000		
Construction		825	375	150	440	1,150	1,000,000	370,000		
Standard	2" - 4" wide	475	200	150	440	975	900,000	330,000		
Utility		225	100	150	440	650	800,000	290,000		
SOUTHERN PINE - Misiones Argentina, Free of Heart Center and Medium Grain Density										
Select Structural	2" & wider	1,700	775	210	710	1,250	1,500,000	550,000	0.54	SPIB
No. 1		1,150	525	210	710	1,150	1,500,000	550,000		
No. 2		1,000	450	210	710	1,100	1,500,000	550,000		
No. 3		575	250	210	710	650	1,400,000	510,000		
Stud	2" & wider	800	350	210	710	700	1,400,000	510,000		
Construction		1,150	525	210	710	1,350	1,400,000	510,000		
Standard	2" - 4" wide	650	300	210	710	1,150	1,300,000	470,000		
Utility		300	125	210	710	750	1,200,000	440,000		

1. **LUMBER DIMENSIONS.** Reference design values are applicable to lumber that will be used under dry conditions such as in most covered structures. For 2" to 4" thick lumber the DRY dressed sizes shall be used (see Table 1A) regardless of the moisture content at the time of manufacture or use. In calculating design values, the natural gain in strength and stiffness that occurs as lumber dries has been taken into consideration as well as the reduction in size that occurs when unseasoned lumber shrinks. The gain in the load carrying capacity due to increased strength and stiffness resulting from drying more than offsets the design effect of size reductions due to shrinkage.

2. Reference design values are applicable only for 2x4 dimensional lumber and shall not be multiplied by the size factor adjustment.

3. When individual species or species groups are combined, the design values to be used for the combination shall be the lowest design values for each individual species or species group for each design property.

4. Does not include states of Baden-Wurttemburg and Saarland.

5. Specific gravity, G, based on weight and volume when oven-dry.

This page left blank intentionally.

Table 5A Adjustment Factors

Volume Factor, C_V

Tabulated bending design values for loading perpendicular to wide faces of laminations, F_{bx}, for structural glued laminated bending members shall be multiplied by the following volume factor:

$$C_V = (21/L)^{1/x}\,(12/d)^{1/x}\,(5.125/b)^{1/x} \leq 1.0$$

where:

> L = length of bending member between points of zero moment, ft
>
> d = depth of bending member, in.
>
> b = width (breadth) of bending member, in. For multiple piece width, b = width of widest piece in the layup. Thus b ≤ 10.75".
>
> x = 20 for Southern Pine
>
> x = 10 for all other species

The volume factor shall not apply simultaneously with the beam stability factor (see 5.3.6). Therefore, the lesser of these adjustment factors shall apply.

Flat Use Factor, C_{fu}

Tabulated bending design values for loading parallel to wide faces of laminations, F_{by}, shall be multiplied by the following flat use factors when the member dimension parallel to wide faces of laminations is less than 12":

Flat Use Factors, C_{fu}

Member dimension parallel to wide faces of laminations	C_{fu}
10-3/4" or 10-1/2"	1.01
8-3/4" or 8-1/2"	1.04
6-3/4"	1.07
5-1/8" or 5"	1.10
3-1/8" or 3"	1.16
2-1/2"	1.19

Wet Service Factor, C_M

When structural glued laminated timber is used whe moisture content will be 16% or greater, design valu shall be multiplied by the appropriate wet service facto from the following table:

Wet Service Factors, C_M

F_b	F_t	F_v	$F_{c\perp}$	F_c	E and E_r
0.8	0.8	0.875	0.53	0.73	0.833

Table 5A Reference Design Values for Structural Glued Laminated Softwood Timber

(Members stressed primarily in bending) (Tabulated design values are for normal load duration and dry service conditions. See NDS 5.3 for a comprehensive description of design value adjustment factors.)

Use with Table 5A Adjustment Factors

| Stress Class | Bending About X-X Axis — Loaded Perpendicular to Wide Faces of Laminations | | | | | | Bending About Y-Y Axis — Loaded Parallel to Wide Faces of Laminations | | | | | Axially Loaded | | Fasteners |
	Bending Bottom of Beam Stressed in Tension (Positive Bending) F_{bx}^{+} (psi)	Bending Top of Beam Stressed in Tension (Negative Bending) F_{bx}^{-} [1] (psi)	Compression Perpendicular to Grain F_{cLx} (psi)	Shear Parallel to Grain F_{vx} [4] (psi)	Modulus of Elasticity For Deflection Calculations E_x (10^6 psi)	Modulus of Elasticity For Stability Calculations $E_{x\,min}$ (10^6 psi)	Bending F_{by} (psi)	Compression Perpendicular to Grain F_{cLy} (psi)	Shear Parallel to Grain F_{vy} [4][5] (psi)	Modulus of Elasticity For Deflection Calculations E_y (10^6 psi)	Modulus of Elasticity For Stability Calculations $E_{y\,min}$ (10^6 psi)	Tension Parallel to Grain F_t (psi)	Compression Parallel to Grain F_c (psi)	Specific Gravity for Fastener Design G
16F-1.3E	1600	925	315	195	1.3	0.69	800	315	170	1.1	0.58	675	925	0.41
20F-1.5E	2000	1100	425	195 [6]	1.5	0.79	800	315	170	1.2	0.63	725	925	0.41
24F-1.7E	2400	1450	500	210 [6]	1.7	0.90	1050	315	185	1.3	0.69	775	1000	0.42
24F-1.8E	2400	1450 [2]	650	265 [3]	1.8	0.95	1450	560	230 [3]	1.6	0.85	1100	1600	0.50 [10]
26F-1.9E [7]	2600	1950	650	265 [3]	1.9	1.00	1600	560	230 [3]	1.6	0.85	1150	1600	0.50 [10]
28F-2.1E SP [7]	2800	2300	805	300	2.1 [9]	1.11 [9]	1600	650	260	1.7	0.90	1250	1750	0.55
30F-2.1E SP [7][8]	3000	2400	805	300	2.1 [9]	1.11 [9]	1750	650	260	1.7	0.90	1250	1750	0.55

1. For balanced layups, F_{bx}^{-} shall be equal to F_{bx}^{+} for the stress class. Designer shall specify when balanced layup is required.
2. The negative reference bending design value, F_{bx}^{-}, is permitted to be increased to 1850 psi for Douglas Fir and to 1950 psi for Southern Pine for specific combinations. Designer shall specify when these increased design values are required.
3. For structural glued laminated timber of Southern Pine, the reference shear design values, F_{vx} and F_{vy}, are permitted to be increased to 300 psi, and 260 psi, respectively.
4. The reference design values for shear, F_{vx} and F_{vy} shall be multiplied by the shear reduction factor, C_{vr}, for the conditions defined in NDS 5.3.10.
5. Reference design values are for timbers with laminations made from a single piece of lumber across the width or multiple pieces that have been edge bonded. For timbers manufactured from multiple piece laminations (across width) that are not edge bonded, the reference design value shall be multiplied by 0.4 for members with 5, 7, or 9 laminations or by 0.5 for all other members. This reduction shall be cumulative with the adjustment in footnote (4).
6. Certain Southern Pine combinations may contain lumber with wane. If lumber with wane is used, the reference design value for shear parallel to grain, F_{vx}, shall be multiplied by 0.67 if wane is allowed on both sides. If wane is limited to one side, F_{vx} shall be multiplied by 0.83. This reduction shall be cumulative with the adjustment in footnote (4).
7. 26F, 28F, and 30F beams are not produced by all manufacturers, therefore, availability may be limited. Contact supplier or manufacturer for details.
8. 30F combinations are restricted to a maximum 6 in. nominal width unless the manufacturer has qualified for wider widths based on full-scale tests subject to approval by an accredited inspection agency.
9. For 28F and 30F members with more than 15 laminations, $E_x = 2.0$ million psi and $E_{x\,min} = 1.06$ million psi.
10. For structural glued laminated timber of Southern Pine, specific gravity for fastener design is permitted to be increased to 0.55.

Stress classes represent groups of similar glued laminated timber combinations. Values for individual combinations are included in Table 5A - Expanded. Reference design values are for members with 4 or more laminations. For 2 and 3 lamination members, see Table 5B. Some stress classes are not available in all species. Contact manufacturer for availability.

Table 5A Expanded – Reference Design Values for Structural Glued Laminated Softwood Timber Combinations[1]

(Members stressed primarily in bending) (Tabulated design values are for normal load duration and dry service conditions. See NDS 5.3 for a comprehensive description of design value adjustment factors.)

Use with Table 5A Adjustment Factors

Combination Symbol	Species Outer/Core	Bending About X-X Axis							Bending About Y-Y Axis					Axially Loaded		Fasteners	
		Bending		Compression Perpendicular to Grain		Shear Parallel to Wide Faces of Laminations	Modulus of Elasticity		Bending	Compression Perpendicular to Grain	Shear Parallel to Grain	Modulus of Elasticity		Tension Parallel to Grain	Compression Parallel to Grain	Specific Gravity for Fastener Design	
		Bottom of Beam Stressed in Tension (Positive Bending) F_{bx}^{+}	Top of Beam Stressed in Tension (Negative Bending) F_{bx}^{-}	Tension Face F_{cLx}	Compression Face F_{cLx}	F_{vx} (2)	E_x (Deflection) / $E_{x\,min}$ (Stability)		F_{by}	F_{cLy}	F_{vy} (2)(3)	E_y (Deflection) / $E_{y\,min}$ (Stability)		F_t	F_c	Top or Bottom Face G	Side Face G
		(psi)	(psi)	(psi)	(psi)	(psi)	(10^6 psi)		(psi)	(psi)	(psi)	(10^6 psi)		(psi)	(psi)		
16F-1.3E		**1600**	**925**	**315**		**195**	**1.3**	**0.69**	**800**	**315**	**170**	**1.1**	**0.58**	**675**	**925**	**0.41**	
16F-V3	DF/DF	1600	1250	560	560	265	1.3	0.79	1450	560	230	1.5	0.79	975	1500	0.50	0.50
16F-V6	DF/DF	1600	1600	560	560	265	1.6	0.85	1450	560	230	1.5	0.79	1000	1600	0.50	0.50
16F-E2	HF/HF	1600	1050	375	375	215	1.4	0.74	1200	375	190	1.3	0.69	825	1150	0.43	0.43
16F-E3	DF/DF	1600	1200	560	560	265	1.6	0.85	1400	560	230	1.5	0.79	975	1600	0.50	0.50
16F-E6	DF/DF	1600	1600	560	560	265	1.6	0.85	1550	560	230	1.5	0.79	1000	1600	0.50	0.50
16F-E7	HF/HF	1600	1600	375	375	215	1.4	0.74	1350	375	190	1.3	0.74	875	1250	0.43	0.43
16F-V2	SP/SP	1600	1400	740	740	300	1.5	0.79	1450	650	260	1.4	0.74	1000	1300	0.55	0.55
16F-V3	SP/SP	1600	1450	740	740	300	1.4	0.74	1450	650	260	1.4	0.74	975	1400	0.55	0.55
16F-V5	SP/SP	1600	1600	650	650	300	1.6	0.85	1600	650	260	1.5	0.79	1000	1550	0.55	0.55
16F-E1	SP/SP	1600	1250	650	650	300	1.6	0.85	1400	650	260	1.6	0.85	1050	1550	0.55	0.55
16F-E3	SP/SP	1600	1600	650	650	300	1.7	0.90	1650	650	260	1.6	0.85	1100	1550	0.55	0.55
20F-1.5E		**2000**	**1100**	**425**		**195**	**1.5**	**0.79**	**800**	**315**	**170**	**1.2**	**0.63**	**725**	**925**	**0.41**	
20F-V3	DF/DF	2000	1450	650	650	265	1.6	0.85	1450	560	230	1.5	0.79	1000	1550	0.50	0.50
20F-V7	DF/DF	2000	2000	650	650	265	1.6	0.85	1450	560	230	1.6	0.85	1050	1600	0.50	0.50
20F-V12	AC/AC	2000	1400	560	560	265	1.5	0.79	1250	470	230	1.4	0.74	925	1500	0.46	0.46
20F-V13	AC/AC	2000	2000	560	560	265	1.5	0.79	1250	470	230	1.4	0.74	950	1550	0.46	0.46
20F-V14	POC/POC	2000	1450	560	560	265	1.5	0.79	1300	470	230	1.4	0.74	900	1600	0.46	0.46
20F-V15	POC/POC	2000	2000	560	560	265	1.5	0.79	1300	470	230	1.4	0.74	900	1600	0.46	0.46
20F-E2	HF/HF	2000	1400	500	500	215	1.6	0.85	1200	375	190	1.4	0.74	925	1350	0.43	0.43
20F-E3	DF/DF	2000	1200	560	560	265	1.7	0.90	1400	560	230	1.7	0.90	1050	1600	0.50	0.50
20F-E6	DF/DF	2000	2000	560	560	265	1.7	0.90	1550	560	230	1.6	0.85	1050	1650	0.50	0.50
20F-E7	HF/HF	2000	2000	500	500	215	1.6	0.85	1450	375	190	1.4	0.74	1050	1450	0.43	0.43
20F-E8	ES/ES	2000	1300	450	450	200	1.5	0.79	1000	315	175	1.4	0.74	825	1100	0.41	0.41
24F-E/SPF1	SPF/SPF	2400	2400	560	560	215	1.6	0.85	1150	470	190	1.6	0.85	1150	2000	0.42	0.42
24F-E/SPF3	SPF/SPF	2400	1550	560	650	215	1.6	0.85	1200	470	195	1.5	0.79	900	1750	0.42	0.42
20F-V2	SP/SP	2000	1550	740	740	300	1.5	0.79	1450	650	260	1.4	0.74	1000	1400	0.55	0.55
20F-V3	SP/SP	2000	1450	650	650	300	1.5	0.79	1600	650	260	1.5	0.79	1000	1400	0.55	0.55
20F-V5	SP/SP	2000	2000	740	740	300	1.6	0.85	1450	650	260	1.4	0.74	1050	1500	0.55	0.55
20F-E1	SP/SP	2000	1300	650	650	300	1.7	0.90	1450	650	260	1.6	0.85	1050	1550	0.55	0.55
20F-E3	SP/SP	2000	1550	650	650	300	1.7	0.90	1700	650	260	1.6	0.85	1150	1600	0.55	0.55
24F-1.7E		**2400**	**1450**	**500**		**210**	**1.7**	**0.90**	**1050**	**315**	**185**	**1.3**	**0.69**	**775**	**1000**	**0.42**	
24F-V5	DF/HF	2400	1600	650	650	215	1.7	0.90	1350	375	200	1.5	0.79	1100	1450	0.50	0.50
24F-V10	DF/HF	2400	2400	650	650	215	1.8	0.95	1450	375	200	1.5	0.79	1100	1550	0.50	0.50
24F-E11	HF/HF	2400	2400	500	500	215	1.8	0.95	1550	375	190	1.5	0.79	1150	1550	0.43	0.43
24F-E15	HF/HF	2400	1600	500	500	215	1.7	0.95	1200	375	190	1.5	0.79	975	1500	0.43	0.43
24F-V1	SP/SP	2400	1750	740	740	300	1.7	0.90	1450	650	260	1.5	0.79	1100	1500	0.55	0.55
24F-V4 (4)	SP/SP	2400	1650	740	740	210	1.7	0.90	1350	470	230	1.5	0.79	975		0.55	

Table 5A Expanded – Reference Design Values for Structural Glued Laminated Softwood Timber Combinations[1] (Cont.)

(Members stressed primarily in bending) (Tabulated design values are for normal load duration and dry service conditions. See NDS 5.3 for a comprehensive description of design value adjustment factors.)

Use with Table 5A Adjustment Factors

Combination Symbol	Species Outer/Core	Bending About X-X Axis (Loaded Perpendicular to Wide Faces of Laminations)							Bending About Y-Y Axis (Loaded Parallel to Wide Faces of Laminations)					Axially Loaded		Fasteners	
		Bending		Compression Perpendicular to Grain		Shear Parallel to Grain	Modulus of Elasticity		Bending	Compression Perpendicular to Grain	Shear Parallel to Grain	Modulus of Elasticity		Tension Parallel to Grain	Compression Parallel to Grain	Specific Gravity for Fastener Design	
		Bottom of Beam Stressed in Tension (Positive Bending) F_{bx}^{+} (psi)	Top of Beam Stressed in Tension (Negative Bending) F_{bx}^{-} (psi)	Tension Face	Compression Face $F_{c\perp x}$ (psi)	F_{vx} [2] (psi)	For Deflection Calculations E_x (10^6 psi)	For Stability Calculations $E_{x\,min}$ (10^6 psi)	F_{by} (psi)	$F_{c\perp y}$ (psi)	F_{vy} [2][3] (psi)	For Deflection Calculations E_y (10^6 psi)	For Stability Calculations $E_{y\,min}$ (10^6 psi)	F_t (psi)	F_c (psi)	Top or Bottom Face	Side Face G
24F-1.8E		**2400**	**1450**	**650**		**265**	**1.8**	**0.95**	**1450**	**560**	**230**	**1.6**	**0.85**	**1100**	**1600**	**0.50**	
24F-V4	DF/DF	2400	1850	650	650	265	1.8	0.95	1450	560	230	1.6	0.85	1100	1650	0.50	0.50
24F-V8	DF/DF	2400	2400	650	650	265	1.8	0.95	1550	560	230	1.6	0.85	1100	1650	0.50	0.50
24F-E4	DF/DF	2400	1450	650	650	265	1.8	0.95	1400	560	230	1.7	0.90	1100	1700	0.50	0.50
24F-E13	DF/DF	2400	2400	650	650	265	1.8	0.95	1750	560	230	1.7	0.90	1250	1700	0.50	0.50
24F-E18	DF/DF	2400	2400	650	650	265	1.8	0.95	1550	560	230	1.7	0.90	975	1700	0.50	0.50
24F-V3	SP/SP	2400	2000	740	740	300	1.8	0.95	1700	650	260	1.6	0.85	1150	1650	0.55	0.55
24F-V8	SP/SP	2400	2400	740	740	300	1.8	0.95	1700	650	260	1.6	0.85	1150	1650	0.55	0.55
24F-E1	SP/SP	2400	1450	805	650	300	1.8	0.95	1550	650	260	1.7	0.90	1150	1600	0.55	0.55
24F-E4	SP/SP	2400	2400	805	805	300	1.9	1.00	1850	650	260	1.8	0.95	1450	1750	0.55	0.55
26F-1.9E [5]		**2600**	**1950**	**650**		**265**	**1.9**	**1.00**	**1600**	**560**	**230**	**1.6**	**0.85**	**1150**	**1600**	**0.50**	
26F-V1	DF/DF	2600	1950	650	650	265	2.0	1.06	1850	560	230	1.8	0.95	1350	1850	0.50	0.50
26F-V2	DF/DF	2600	2600	650	650	265	2.0	1.06	1850	560	230	1.8	0.95	1350	1850	0.50	0.50
26F-V1	SP/SP	2600	2000	740	740	300	1.8	0.95	1700	650	260	1.6	0.85	1150	1600	0.55	0.55
26F-V2	SP/SP	2600	2100	740	740	300	1.9	1.00	1950	740	260	1.8	0.95	1300	1850	0.55	0.55
26F-V3	SP/SP	2600	2100	740	740	300	1.9	1.00	1950	650	260	1.8	0.95	1250	1800	0.55	0.55
26F-V4	SP/SP	2600	2600	740	740	300	1.9	1.00	1700	650	260	1.8	0.95	1200	1600	0.55	0.55
26F-V5	SP/SP	2600	2600	740	740	300	1.9	1.00	1950	650	260	1.8	0.95	1300	1850	0.55	0.55
28F-2.1E SP [5]		**2800**	**2300**	**805**		**300**	**2.1** [7]	**1.11** [7]	**1600**	**650**	**260**	**1.7**	**0.90**	**1250**	**1750**	**0.55**	
28F-E1	SP/SP	2800	2300	805	805	300	2.1 [7]	1.11 [7]	1600	650	260	1.7	0.90	1300	1850	0.55	0.55
28F-E2	SP/SP	2800	2800	805	805	300	2.1 [7]	1.11 [7]	2000	650	260	1.7	0.90	1300	1850	0.55	0.55
30F-2.1E SP [5][6]		**3000**	**2400**	**805**		**300**	**2.1** [7]	**1.11** [7]	**1750**	**650**	**260**	**1.7**	**0.90**	**1250**	**1750**	**0.55**	
30F-E1	SP/SP	3000	2400	805	805	300	2.1 [7]	1.11 [7]	1750	650	260	1.7	0.90	1250	1750	0.55	0.55
30F-E2	SP/SP	3000	3000	805	805	300	2.1 [7]	1.11 [7]	1750	650	260	1.7	0.90	1350	1750	0.55	0.55

1. The combinations in this table are applicable to members consisting of 4 or more laminations and are intended primarily for members stressed in bending due to loads applied perpendicular to the wide faces of the laminations. However, reference design values are tabulated for loading both perpendicular and parallel to the wide faces of the laminations. For combinations and reference design values applicable to members loaded primarily axially or parallel to the wide faces of the laminations, see Table 5B. For members of 2 or 3 laminations, see Table 5B.
2. The reference design values for shear, F_{vx} and F_{vy}, shall be multiplied by the shear reduction factor, C_{vr}, for the conditions defined in NDS 5.3.10.
3. Reference design values are for structural glued laminated timbers with laminations made from a single piece of lumber across the width or multiple pieces that have been edge bonded. For structural glued laminated timber manufactured from multiple piece laminations (across width) that are not edge-bonded, value shall be multiplied by 0.4 for members with 5, 7, or 9 laminations or by 0.5 for all other members. This reduction shall be cumulative with the adjustment in footnote 2.
4. This combination may contain lumber with wane. If lumber with wane is used, the reference design value for shear parallel to grain, F_{vx}, shall be multiplied by 0.67 if wane is allowed on both sides. If wane is limited to one side, F_{vx} shall be multiplied by 0.83. This reduction shall be cumulative with the adjustment in footnote 2.
5. 26F, 28F, and 30F beams are not produced by all manufacturers, therefore, availability may be limited. Contact supplier or manufacturer for details.
6. 30F combinations are restricted to a maximum 6 in. nominal width unless the manufacturer has qualified for wider widths based on full-scale tests subject to approval by an accredited inspection agency.
7. For 28F and 30F members with more than 15 laminations, $E_x = 2.0$ million psi and $E_{x\,min} = 1.06$ million psi.

4

REFERENCE DESIGN VALUES

Volume Factor, C_V

Tabulated bending design values for loading perpendicular to wide faces of laminations, F_{bx}, for structural glued laminated bending members shall be multiplied by the following volume factor:

$$C_V = (21/L)^{1/x} (12/d)^{1/x} (5.125/b)^{1/x} \le 1.0$$

where:

L = length of bending member between points of zero moment, ft

d = depth of bending member, in.

b = width (breadth) of bending member, in. For multiple piece width layups, b = width of widest piece in the layup. Thus $b \le 10.75$".

x = 20 for Southern Pine

x = 10 for all other species

The volume factor shall not apply simultaneously with the beam stability factor (see 5.3.6). Therefore, the lesser of these adjustment factors shall apply.

Wet Service Factor, C_M

When structural glued laminated timber is used where moisture content will be 16% or greater, design values shall be multiplied by the appropriate wet service factors from the following table:

Wet Service Factors, C_M

F_b	F_t	F_v	$F_{c\perp}$	F_c	E and E_{min}
0.8	0.8	0.875	0.53	0.73	0.833

Flat Use Factor, C_{fu}

Tabulated bending design values for loading parallel to wide faces of laminations, F_{by}, shall be multiplied by the following flat use factors when the member dimension parallel to wide faces of laminations is less than 12":

Flat Use Factors, C_{fu}

Member dimension parallel to wide faces of laminations	C_{fu}
10-3/4" or 10-1/2"	1.01
8-3/4" or 8-1/2"	1.04
6-3/4"	1.07
5-1/8" or 5"	1.10
3-1/8" or 3"	1.16
2-1/2"	1.19

Table 5B Reference Design Values for Structural Glued Laminated Softwood Timber

(Members stressed primarily in axial tension or compression) (Tabulated design values are for normal load duration and dry service conditions. See NDS 5.3 for a comprehensive description of design value adjustment factors.)

Use with Table 5B Adjustment Factors

Combination Symbol	Species	Grade	All Loading — Modulus of Elasticity — For Deflection Calculations E (10⁶ psi)	All Loading — Modulus of Elasticity — For Stability Calculations Emin (10⁶ psi)	Compression Perpendicular to Grain Fc⊥ (psi)	Axially Loaded — Tension Parallel to Grain — 2 or More Laminations Ft (psi)	Axially Loaded — Compression Parallel to Grain — 4 or More Laminations Fc (psi)	Axially Loaded — Compression Parallel to Grain — 2 or 3 Laminations Fc (psi)	Bending about Y-Y Axis — Bending — 4 or More Laminations Fby (psi)	Bending about Y-Y Axis — Bending — 3 Laminations Fby (psi)	Bending about Y-Y Axis — Bending — 2 Laminations Fby (psi)	Bending about Y-Y Axis — Shear Parallel to Grain[1][2][3] Fvy (psi)	Bending About X-X Axis — Bending — 2 Laminations to 15 in. Deep[4] Fbx (psi)	Bending About X-X Axis — Shear Parallel to Grain[3] Fvx (psi)	Specific Gravity for Fastener Design G
Visually Graded Western Species															
1	DF	L3	1.5	0.79	560	950	1550	1250	1450	1250	1000	230	1250	265	0.50
2	DF	L2	1.6	0.85	560	1250	1950	1600	1800	1600	1300	230	1700	265	0.50
3	DF	L2D	1.9	1.00	650	1450	2300	1900	2100	1850	1550	230	2000	265	0.50
4	DF	L1CL	1.9	1.00	590	1400	2100	1950	2200	2000	1650	230	2100	265	0.50
5	DF	L1	2.0	1.06	650	1650	2400	2100	2400	2100	1800	230	2200	265	0.50
14	HF	L3	1.4	0.69	375	800	1100	1050	1200	1050	850	190	1100	215	0.43
15	HF	L2	1.4	0.74	375	1050	1350	1350	1500	1350	1100	190	1450	215	0.43
16	HF	L1	1.6	0.85	375	1200	1500	1500	1750	1550	1300	190	1600	215	0.43
17	HF	L1D	1.7	0.90	500	1400	1750	1750	2000	1850	1550	190	1900	215	0.43
22[5]	SW	L3	1.0	0.53	315	525	850	725	800	700	575	170	725	195	0.35
69	AC	L3	1.2	0.63	470	725	1150	1100	1100	975	775	230	1000	265	0.46
70	AC	L2	1.3	0.69	470	975	1450	1450	1400	1250	1000	230	1350	265	0.46
71	AC	L1D	1.6	0.85	560	1250	1900	1900	1850	1650	1400	230	1750	265	0.46
72	AC	L1S	1.6	0.85	560	1250	1900	1900	1850	1650	1400	230	1900	265	0.46
73	POC	L3	1.3	0.69	470	775	1500	1200	1200	1050	825	230	1050	265	0.46
74	POC	L2	1.4	0.74	470	1050	1900	1550	1450	1300	1100	230	1400	265	0.46
75	POC	L1D	1.7	0.90	560	1350	2300	2050	1950	1750	1500	230	1850	265	0.46
Visually Graded Southern Pine															
47	SP	N2M12	1.4	0.74	650	1200	1900	1150	1750	1550	1300	260	1400	300	0.55
47 1:10	SP	N2M10	1.4	0.74	650	1150	1700	1150	1750	1550	1300	260	1400	300	0.55
47 1:8	SP	N2M	1.4	0.74	650	1000	1500	1150	1600	1550	1300	260	1400	300	0.55
48	SP	N2D12	1.7	0.90	740	1400	2200	1350	2000	1800	1500	260	1600	300	0.55
48 1:10	SP	N2D10	1.7	0.90	740	1350	1750	1350	1850	1800	1500	260	1600	300	0.55
48 1:8	SP	N2D	1.7	0.90	740	1150	2100	1350	1950	1800	1500	260	1800	300	0.55
49	SP	N1M16	1.7	0.90	650	1350	1750	1450	1950	1750	1500	260	1800	300	0.55
49 1:14	SP	N1M14	1.7	0.90	650	1350	2100	1450	1950	1750	1500	260	1800	300	0.55
49 1:12	SP	N1M12	1.7	0.90	650	1350	2000	1450	1950	1750	1500	260	1800	300	0.55
49 1:10	SP	N1M	1.7	0.90	650	1300	1700	1450	1850	1750	1500	260	1800	300	0.55
50	SP	N1D14	1.9	1.00	740	1550	2300	1700	2300	2100	1750	260	2100	300	0.55
50 1:12	SP	N1D12	1.9	1.00	740	1500	2200	1700	2300	2100	1750	260	2100	300	0.55
50 1:10	SP	N1D	1.9	1.00	740	1350	2000	1700	2300	2100	1750	260	2100	300	0.55

1. For members with 2 or 3 laminations, the reference shear design value for transverse loads parallel to the wide faces of the laminations, F_{vy}, shall be reduced by multiplying by a factor of 0.84 or 0.95, respectively.
2. The reference shear design value for transverse loads applied parallel to the wide faces of the laminations, F_{vy}, shall be multiplied by 0.4 for members with 5, 7, or 9 laminations manufactured from multiple piece laminations (across width) that are not edge bonded. The reference shear design value, F_{vy}, shall be multiplied by 0.5 for all other members manufactured from multiple piece laminations with unbonded edge joints. This reduction shall be cumulative with the adjustments in footnotes 1 and 3.
3. The reference design values for shear, F_{vx} and F_{vy}, shall be multiplied by the shear reduction factor, C_{vr}, for the conditions defined in NDS 5.3.10.
4. For members greater than 15 in. deep, the reference bending design value, F_{bx}, shall be reduced by multiplying by a factor of 0.88.
5. When Western Cedars, Western Cedars (North), Western Woods, and Redwood (open grain) are used in combinations for Softwood Species (SW), the reference design value for modulus of elasticity, E, shall be reduced by 100,000 psi and E_{min} shall be reduced by 52,800 psi. When Coast Sitka Spruce, Coast Species, Western White Pine, and Eastern White Pine are used in combinations for Softwood Species (SW) reference design values for shear parallel to grain, F_{vx} and F_{vy}, shall be reduced by 10 psi, before applying any other adjustments.

Table 5C Adjustment Factors

Volume Factor, C_V

Tabulated bending design values for loading perpendicular to wide faces of laminations, F_{bx}, for structural glued laminated bending members shall be multiplied by the following volume factor:

$$C_V = (21/L)^{1/10} (12/d)^{1/10} (5.125/b)^{1/10} \leq 1.0$$

where:

L = length of bending member between points of zero moment, ft

d = depth of bending member, in.

b = width (breadth) of bending member, in. For multiple piece width layups, b = width of widest piece in the layup. Thus $b \leq 10.75$".

The volume factor shall not apply simultaneously with the beam stability factor (see 5.3.6). Therefore, the lesser of these adjustment factors shall apply.

Wet Service Factor, C_M

When structural glued laminated timber is used where moisture content will be 16% or greater, design values shall be multiplied by the appropriate wet service factors from the following table:

Wet Service Factors, C_M

F_b	F_t	F_v	$F_{c\perp}$	F_c	E and E_{min}
0.8	0.8	0.875	0.53	0.73	0.833

Flat Use Factor, C_{fu}

Tabulated bending design values for loading parallel to wide faces of laminations, F_{by}, shall be multiplied by the following flat use factors when the member dimension parallel to wide faces of laminations is less than 12":

Flat Use Factors, C_{fu}

Member dimension parallel to wide faces of laminations	C_{fu}
10-3/4" or 10-1/2"	1.01
8-3/4" or 8-1/2"	1.04
6-3/4"	1.07
5-1/8" or 5"	1.10
3-1/8" or 3"	1.16
2-1/2"	1.19

Table 5C Reference Design Values for Structural Glued Laminated Hardwood Timber[1]

(Members stressed primarily in bending) (Tabulated design values are for normal load duration and dry service conditions. See NDS 5.3 for a comprehensive description of design value adjustment factors.)

Use with Table 5C Adjustment Factors

Combination Symbol	Bending About X-X Axis (Loaded Perpendicular to Wide Faces of Laminations)						Bending About Y-Y Axis (Loaded Parallel to Wide Faces of Laminations)					Axially Loaded		Fasteners[3]
	Bending Bottom of Beam Stressed in Tension (Positive Bending) F_{bx}^{+} (psi)	Bending Top of Beam Stressed in Tension (Negative Bending) F_{bx}^{-} (psi)	Compression Perpendicular to Grain $F_{c\perp x}$ (psi)	Shear Parallel to Grain (Horizontal) F_{vx} (psi)	Modulus of Elasticity For Deflection Calculations E_x (10^6 psi)	Modulus of Elasticity For Stability Calculations $E_{x\,min}$ (10^6 psi)	Bending F_{by} (psi)	Compression Perpendicular to Grain $F_{c\perp y}$ (psi)	Shear Parallel to Grain (Horizontal) F_{vy}[2] (psi)	Modulus of Elasticity For Deflection Calculations E_y (10^6 psi)	Modulus of Elasticity For Stability Calculations $E_{y\,min}$ (10^6 psi)	Tension Parallel to Grain F_t (psi)	Compression Parallel to Grain F_c (psi)	Specific Gravity for Fastener Design G
Visually Graded Hardwoods														
12F-V1	1200	600	285	125	1.2	0.63	1050	285	110	1.0	0.53	600	800	0.39
12F-V2	1200	1200	285	125	1.2	0.63	1050	285	110	1.1	0.58	625	860	0.39
14F-V1	1400	700	405	155	1.3	0.69	1250	405	135	1.1	0.58	700	950	0.45
14F-V2	1400	700	590	180	1.3	0.69	1450	590	160	1.1	0.58	750	1200	0.53
14F-V3	1400	1400	405	155	1.3	0.69	1250	405	135	1.1	0.58	725	950	0.45
14F-V4	1400	1400	590	180	1.3	0.69	1450	590	160	1.1	0.58	775	1200	0.53
16F-V1	1600	800	590	180	1.4	0.74	1400	590	160	1.2	0.63	800	1200	0.53
16F-V2	1600	800	835	200	1.5	0.79	1700	835	175	1.3	0.69	875	1250	0.63
16F-V3	1600	1600	590	180	1.4	0.74	1400	590	160	1.2	0.63	850	1200	0.53
16F-V4	1600	1600	835	200	1.6	0.85	1700	835	175	1.3	0.69	900	1300	0.63
20F-V1	2000	1000	835	200	1.7	0.90	1700	835	175	1.4	0.74	975	1400	0.63
20F-V2	2000	2000	835	200	1.7	0.90	1700	835	175	1.4	0.74	1000	1400	0.63
E-Rated Hardwoods														
16F-E1	1600	800	440	125	1.4	0.74	1250	285	110	1.2	0.63	825	975	0.39
16F-E2	1600	1600	440	125	1.4	0.74	1400	285	110	1.2	0.63	900	1000	0.39
20F-E1	2000	1000	590	155	1.6	0.85	1350	405	135	1.3	0.69	950	1050	0.45
20F-E2	2000	2000	590	155	1.6	0.85	1600	405	135	1.3	0.69	1050	1100	0.45
24F-E1	2400	1200	770	180	1.8	0.95	1550	590	160	1.5	0.79	1050	1400	0.53
24F-E2	2400	2400	770	180	1.8	0.95	1650	590	160	1.5	0.79	1050	1400	0.53
24F-E3 YP	2400	1200	590	155	1.8	0.95	1450	405	135	1.5	0.79	975	1200	0.45
24F-E4 RM	2400	1200	895	220	1.8	0.95	1650	710	195	1.6	0.85	1050	1350	0.53
24F-E5 RO	2400	1200	1075	235	1.8	0.95	1700	900	205	1.5	0.79	1100	1450	0.63

1. The combinations in this table are applicable to members consisting of 4 or more laminations and are intended primarily for members stressed in bending due to loads applied perpendicular to the wide faces of the laminations. However, reference design values are tabulated for loading both perpendicular and parallel to the wide faces of the laminations. For combinations and reference design values for members loaded primarily axially or parallel to the wide faces of the laminations, see Table 5D.
2. Reference design values are for timbers with laminations made from a single piece of lumber across the width or multiple pieces that have been edge bonded. For timbers manufactured from multiple piece laminations (across width) that are not edge bonded, value shall be multiplied by 0.4 for members with 5, 7, or 9 laminations or by 0.5 for all other members.
3. Fastener values are for groups of hardwood species permitted in each combination. If actual species is known, values for that species are permitted to be used.

This page left blank intentionally.

Table 5D Adjustment Factors

Volume Factor, C_V

Tabulated bending design values for loading perpendicular to wide faces of laminations, F_{bx}, for structural glued laminated bending members shall be multiplied by the following volume factor:

$$C_V = (21/L)^{1/10} (12/d)^{1/10} (5.125/b)^{1/10} \le 1.0$$

where:

     L = length of bending member between points of zero moment, ft

     d = depth of bending member, in.

     b = width (breadth) of bending member, in. For multiple piece width layups, b = width of widest piece in the layup. Thus $b \le 10.75"$.

The volume factor shall not apply simultaneously with the beam stability factor (see 5.3.6). Therefore, the lesser of these adjustment factors shall apply.

Wet Service Factor, C_M

When structural glued laminated timber is used where moisture content will be 16% or greater, design values shall be multiplied by the appropriate wet service factors from the following table:

Wet Service Factors, C_M

F_b	F_t	F_v	$F_{c\perp}$	F_c	E and E_{min}
0.8	0.8	0.875	0.53	0.73	0.833

Flat Use Factor, C_{fu}

Tabulated bending design values for loading parallel to wide faces of laminations, F_{by}, shall be multiplied by the following flat use factors when the member dimension parallel to wide faces of laminations is less than 12":

Flat Use Factors, C_{fu}

Member dimension parallel to wide faces of laminations	C_{fu}
10-3/4" or 10-1/2"	1.01
8-3/4" or 8-1/2"	1.04
6-3/4"	1.07
5-1/8" or 5"	1.10
3-1/8" or 3"	1.16
2-1/2"	1.19

4

REFERENCE DESIGN VALUES

Table 5D Reference Design Values for Structural Glued Laminated Hardwood Timber

(Members stressed primarily in axial tension or compression) (Tabulated design values are for normal load duration and dry service conditions. See NDS 5.3 for a comprehensive description of design value adjustment factors.)

Use with Table 5D Adjustment Factors

Combination Symbol	Species Group	Grade	All Loading — Modulus of Elasticity — E For Deflection Calculations (10⁶ psi)	All Loading — Modulus of Elasticity — E_min For Stability Calculations (10⁶ psi)	All Loading — Compression Perpendicular to Grain F_cperp (psi)	Axially Loaded — Tension Parallel to Grain 2 or More Lami-nations F_t (psi)	Axially Loaded — Compression Parallel to Grain 4 or More Lami-nations F_c (psi)	Axially Loaded — Compression Parallel to Grain 2 or 3 Lami-nations F_c (psi)	Bending about Y-Y Axis — Bending 4 or More Lami-nations F_by (psi)	Bending about Y-Y Axis — Bending 3 Lami-nations F_by (psi)	Bending about Y-Y Axis — Bending 2 Lami-nations F_by (psi)	Bending about Y-Y Axis — Shear Parallel to Grain 4 or More Lami-nations F_vy (psi)	Bending About X-X Axis — Bending 2 Lami-nations to 15 in. Deep F_bx (psi)	Bending About X-X Axis — Shear Parallel to Grain F_vx (psi)	Fasteners — Specific Gravity for Fastener Design G
Visually Graded Hardwoods															
H1	A	N3	1.3	0.67	835	425	900	900	1250	1100	875	175	925	200	0.63
H2	A	N2	1.5	0.78	835	875	1300	1300	1700	1550	1300	175	1200	200	0.63
H3	A	N1	1.7	0.88	835	1000	1450	1450	2000	1800	1550	175	1600	200	0.63
H4	A	SS	1.7	0.88	835	1150	1600	1600	2000	1850	1600	175	1700	200	0.63
H5	B	N3	1.2	0.62	590	350	800	800	1050	900	750	160	750	180	0.53
H6	B	N2	1.3	0.67	590	750	1150	1150	1450	1300	1050	160	1000	180	0.53
H7	B	N1	1.5	0.78	590	850	1300	1300	1650	1500	1300	160	1350	180	0.53
H8	B	SS	1.5	0.78	590	950	1450	1450	1700	1550	1350	160	1400	180	0.53
H9	C	N3	1.0	0.52	405	300	625	625	900	800	625	135	675	155	0.45
H10	C	N2	1.2	0.62	405	625	900	900	1200	1100	925	135	875	155	0.45
H11	C	N1	1.3	0.67	405	725	1000	1000	1400	1300	1100	135	1150	155	0.45
H12	C	SS	1.3	0.67	405	825	1100	1100	1450	1350	1150	135	1200	155	0.45
H13	D	N3	0.9	0.47	285	250	575	575	775	675	550	110	575	125	0.39
H14	D	N2	1.1	0.57	285	550	825	825	1050	950	800	110	750	125	0.39
H15	D	N1	1.2	0.62	285	625	925	925	1200	1100	950	110	1000	125	0.39
H16	D	SS	1.2	0.62	285	700	1050	1050	1250	1150	1000	110	1050	125	0.39

Table 5D Reference Design Values for Structural Glued Laminated Hardwood Timber (Cont.)

(Members stressed primarily in axial tension or compression) (Tabulated design values are for normal load duration and dry service conditions. See NDS 5.3 for a comprehensive description of design value adjustment factors.)

Use with Table 5D Adjustment Factors

Combination Symbol	Species Group	Grade	All Loading — Modulus of Elasticity — For Deflection Calculations — E (10⁶ psi)	All Loading — Modulus of Elasticity — For Stability Calculations — E_min (10⁶ psi)	All Loading — Compression Perpendicular to Grain — F_cperp (psi)	Axially Loaded — Tension Parallel to Grain — 2 or More Laminations — F_t (psi)	Axially Loaded — Compression Parallel to Grain — 4 or More Laminations — F_c (psi)	Axially Loaded — Compression Parallel to Grain — 2 or 3 Laminations — F_c (psi)	Bending about Y-Y Axis — Bending — 4 or More Laminations — F_by (psi)	Bending about Y-Y Axis — Bending — 3 Laminations — F_by (psi)	Bending about Y-Y Axis — Bending — 2 Laminations — F_by (psi)	Bending about Y-Y Axis — Shear Parallel to Grain[1][2] — 4 or More Laminations — F_vy (psi)	Bending About X-X Axis — Bending — 2 Laminations to 15 in. Deep[3] — F_bx (psi)	Bending About X-X Axis — Shear Parallel to Grain — F_vx (psi)	Fasteners — Specific Gravity for Fastener Design — G
E-Rated Hardwoods															
H17	A	1.5E3	1.4	0.73	1015	1000	1500	1350	1850	1750	1550	175	1200	200	0.63
H18	A	1.8E3	1.7	0.88	1015	1150	1950	1850	2100	2000	1750	175	1450	200	0.63
H19	A	1.8E6	1.7	0.88	1015	1450	2000	1900	2300	2200	1950	175	1650	200	0.63
H20	A	2.0E3	1.9	0.98	1015	1350	2600	2200	2400	2300	2100	175	1700	200	0.63
H21	A	2.0E6	1.9	0.98	1015	1700	2430	2300	2400	2400	2300	175	2100	200	0.63
H22	B	1.5E3	1.4	0.73	770	1000	1500	1350	1850	1750	1550	160	1200	180	0.53
H23	B	1.8E3	1.7	0.88	770	1150	1950	1850	2100	2000	1750	160	1450	180	0.53
H24	B	1.8E6	1.7	0.88	770	1450	2000	1900	2300	2200	1950	160	1650	180	0.53
H25	B	2.0E3	1.9	0.98	770	1350	2300	2200	2400	2300	2100	160	1700	180	0.53
H26	B	2.0E6	1.9	0.98	770	1700	2400	2300	2400	2400	2300	160	2100	180	0.53
H27	C	1.5E3	1.4	0.73	590	1000	1500	1350	1850	1750	1550	135	1200	155	0.45
H28	C	1.8E3	1.7	0.88	590	1150	1950	1850	2100	2000	1750	135	1450	155	0.45
H29	C	1.8E6	1.7	0.88	590	1450	2000	1900	2300	2200	1950	135	1650	155	0.45
H30	C	2.0E3	1.9	0.98	590	1350	2300	2200	2400	2300	2100	135	1700	155	0.45
H31	C	2.0E6	1.9	0.98	590	1700	2400	2300	2400	2400	2300	135	2100	155	0.45
H32	D	1.5E3	1.4	0.73	440	1000	1500	1350	1850	1750	1550	110	1200	125	0.39
H33	D	1.5E6	1.4	0.73	440	1250	1500	1400	2000	1900	1700	110	1250	125	0.39
H34	D	1.8E3	1.7	0.88	440	1150	1950	1850	2100	2000	1750	110	1450	125	0.39
H35	D	1.8E6	1.7	0.88	440	1450	2000	1900	2300	2200	1950	110	1650	125	0.39
H36	D	2.0E3	1.9	0.98	440	1350	2300	2200	2400	2300	2100	110	1700	125	0.39
H37	D	2.0E6	1.9	0.98	440	1700	2400	2300	2400	2400	2300	110	2100	125	0.39

1. For members with 2 or 3 laminations, the reference shear design value for transverse loads parallel to the wide faces of the laminations, F_{vy}, shall be reduced by multiplying by a factor of 0.84 or 0.95, respectively. The reference shear design value for transverse loads applied parallel to the wide faces of the laminations, F_{vy}, shall be multiplied by 0.4 for members with 5, 7, or 9 laminations manufactured from multiple piece laminations (across width) that are not edge bonded. The reference shear design value, F_{vy}, shall be multiplied by 0.5 for all other members manufactured from multiple piece laminations with unbonded edge joints. This reduction shall be cumulative with the adjustment in footnote (1).
3. For members greater than 15 in. deep, the reference bending design value, F_{bx}, shall be reduced by multiplying by a factor of 0.88.

4

REFERENCE DESIGN VALUES

Condition Treatment Factor, C_{ct}

Reference design values are based on air dried conditioning. If kiln-drying, steam-conditioning, or boultonizing is used prior to treatment then the reference design values shall be multiplied by the condition treatment factors, C_{ct}.

Condition Treatment Factor, C_{ct}

Air Dried	Kiln Dried	Boulton Drying	Steaming (Normal)	Steaming (Marine)
1.0	0.90	0.95	0.80	0.74

Critical Section Factor, C_{cs}

Reference compression design values parallel to grain, F_c, for round timber piles and poles are based on the strength at the tip of the pile. Reference compression design values parallel to grain, F_c, in Table 6A and Table 6B shall be permitted to be multiplied by the critical section factor. The critical section factor, C_{cs}, shall be determined as follows:

$$C_{cs} = 1.0 + 0.004L_c$$

where:

L_c = length from tip of pile to critical section, ft

The increase for location of critical section shall not exceed 10% for any pile or pole ($C_{cs} \leq 1.10$). The critical section factors, C_{cs}, are independent of tapered column provisions in NDS 3.7.2 and both shall be permitted to be used in design calculations.

Load Sharing Factor (Pile Group Factor), C_{ls}

For piles, reference design values are based on sing piles. If multiple piles are connected by concrete caps e equivalent force distributing elements so that the pile grou deforms as a single element when subjected to the loa effects imposed on the element, reference bending desig values, F_b, and reference compression design values para lel to the grain, F_c, shall be permitted to be multiplied b the load sharing factors, C_{ls}.

Load Sharing Factor, C_{ls}

Reference Design Value	Number of Piles in Group	C_{ls}
F_c	2	1.06
	3	1.09
	4 or more	1.11
F_b	2	1.05
	3	1.07
	4 or more	1.08

Size Factor, C_F

For poles and piles with a diameter greater than 13.5 reference bending design values shall be multiplied b the following size factor determined on the basis of a equivalent conventionally loaded square beam of the sam cross-sectional area:

$$C_F = (12/d)^{1/9}$$

Table 6A   Reference Design Values for Treated Round Timber Piles Graded per ASTM D25

(Tabulated design values are for normal load duration and wet service conditions. See NDS 6.3 for a comprehensive description of design value adjustment factors.)

| Species | Design values in pounds per square inch (psi) | | | | | | Specific Gravity[4] |
| | Bending F_b | Shear parallel to grain F_v | Compression perpendicular to grain $F_{c\perp}$ | Compression parallel to grain F_c | Modulus of elasticity | | |
					E	E_{min}	G
Pacific Coast Douglas Fir[1]	2,050	160	490	1,300	1,700,000	690,000	0.50
Red Pine[2]	1,350	125	270	850	1,300,000	520,000	0.42
Southern Pine (Grouped)[3]	1,950	160	440	1,250	1,500,000	600,000	0.55

1. Pacific Coast Douglas Fir reference design values apply to this species as defined in ASTM Standard D 1760.
2. Red Pine reference design values apply to Red Pine grown in the United States.
3. Southern Pine reference design values apply to Loblolly, Longleaf, Shortleaf, and Slash Pines.
4. Specific gravity, G, based on weight and volume when oven-dry.

Table 6B   Reference Design Values for Round Timber Construction Poles Graded per ASTM D3200

(Tabulated design values are for normal load duration and wet service conditions. See NDS 6.3 for a comprehensive description of design value adjustment factors.)

| Species | Design values in pounds per square inch (psi) | | | | | | Specific Gravity[4] |
| | Bending F_b | Shear parallel to grain F_v | Compression perpendicular to grain $F_{c\perp}$ | Compression parallel to grain F_c | Modulus of elasticity | | |
					E	E_{min}	G
Pacific Coast Douglas Fir[1]	2,050	160	490	1,300	1,700,000	690,000	0.50
Lodgepole Pine	1,275	125	265	825	1,100,000	430,000	0.42
Ponderosa Pine	1,200	175	295	775	1,000,000	400,000	0.43
Red Pine[2]	1,350	125	270	850	1,300,000	520,000	0.42
Southern Pine (Grouped)[3]	1,950	160	440	1,250	1,500,000	600,000	0.55
Western Hemlock	1,550	165	275	1,050	1,300,000	560,000	0.47
Western Larch	1,900	170	405	1,250	1,500,000	660,000	0.49
Western Red Cedar	1,250	140	260	875	1,000,000	360,000	0.34

1. Pacific Coast Douglas Fir reference design values apply to this species as defined in ASTM Standard D 1760.
2. Red Pine reference design values apply to Red Pine grown in the United States.
3. Southern Pine reference design values apply to Loblolly, Longleaf, Shortleaf, and Slash Pines.
4. Specific gravity, G, based on weight and volume when oven-dry.

4

REFERENCE DESIGN VALUES

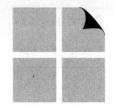